DANCE TO A
DOLPHIN'S SONG

DANCE
TO A
DOLPHIN'S
SONG

The story of a quest for the magic
healing power of the dolphin

Horace Dobbs

JONATHAN CAPE
LONDON

First published 1990
Reprinted 1991, 1997
© Horace Dobbs 1990
Jonathan Cape Ltd, 20 Vauxhall Bridge Road, London SW1V 2SA

Horace Dobbs has asserted his right
to be identified as the author of this work

A CIP catalogue record for this book
is available from the British Library

ISBN 0–224–02628–3 hardback
0–224–03076–0 paperback

Phototypeset by Computape (Pickering) Ltd, North Yorkshire
Printed in Great Britian by
Mackays of Chatham PLC

Contents

Illustrations

With the exception of no. 1 (by Ken Wright) and no. 17 (by Tony Stacey), all photographs are © Horace Dobbs

Listen carefully to the wind, for it brushes
the soul of all living things. Some small particle
of everything it touches is borne with it
on its travels.

Bill Schul
The Psychic Power of Animals

Dedication

In Ancient Greece it was thought
That nothing diviner than a dolphin
Had ever been created.
It was thought they were once men,
Who had lived in cities, along with mortals;
That they had exchanged the land for the sea,
Taking the form of fishes;
But that they had retained the righteous spirit of man,
Retained human thought, and could perform human
    deeds.
Because of this, the killing of a dolphin
Carried the penalty of death . . .
A punishment which may yet be on the books.

When I first heard Heathcote Williams recite these lines from
his epic poem *Whale Nation* they raised in my mind, yet again,
the question of what the Ancient Greeks knew about dolphins
that has since disappeared in the mists of time separating our
two cultures. In the intervening years we have filled libraries
with countless volumes of books, and museums with models of
prehistoric monsters and whales; we have persuaded dolphins
to jump through hoops at given signals, and amassed mountains of scientific data on dolphin sounds. Yet nowhere, in this
vast array of knowledge, are there any of those hard facts, so
beloved of scientists and politicians, to support the case for
dolphins possessing exceptional intelligence, or being worthy
of the status they were accorded two thousand years ago.

So were the Ancient Greeks wrong?

One person whom I feel sure would have said 'No' emphatically to this suggestion was the late Peter Worswick. I never met Peter but I got to know him well through a number of long letters I received from him. In them he wrote of the immense attraction he felt towards dolphins and how he arranged his life and his meagre finances around going to see them in dolphinariums. These pilgrimages were like visits to beloved relatives in a hospice – meeting the dolphins gave him great joy, but the circumstances in which he found them filled him with even greater grief. He felt that being imprisoned in small, sometimes grubby pools was degrading for the dolphins, and even more so for the humans who denied the dolphins their freedom to roam the seas. At the time of our correspondence Percy, a friendly wild dolphin, was cavorting off the coast of Cornwall. I wrote to Peter suggesting that he should make his way to Portreath to see Bob Holborn, one of the dolphin's special human friends, saying I felt sure Bob would take him out in his inflatable to see Percy. I heard no more from Peter Worswick.

A couple of years later, however, the subject of Peter cropped up in a phone conversation with Bob's wife Judy. She told me that a tall man, with long blond hair and Jesus sandals had arrived at their guest house with very little money having hitch-hiked from the Midlands. His baggage consisted of a brief-case packed with pictures of dolphins, all carefully mounted, and neatly labelled with details of their names, and the dates of his visits. With typical generosity Judy took the stranger in, fed him, and gave him free accommodation.

The next day Bob took him out in his inflatable. As Peter couldn't swim, Bob encased his visitor in a thick wetsuit, to give him buoyancy, produced a rope for him to hold on to, and set him afloat in the sea with Percy.

When Percy simply vanished from the scene at the end of the summer in 1984 Bob was distraught. He and Judy moved away from Portreath, and for a time took jobs as assistant administrators at Lanhydrock House, the National Trust picture gallery and garden in Bodmin. It was there that the Holborns received a phone call from Peter's parents telling them of their son's death.

Peter had been living in rooms when it happened. One day he was changing the water in a tank containing his pet terrapins when he was called away. On his return he found that the water had overflowed and ruined his entire collection of dolphin pictures – including those of himself in the sea with Percy. The prospect of living without them was so distressing that Peter took his own life.

When they were going through his belongings, Peter's parents found the Holborns' address and contacted them. They spoke of Peter's encounter in the sea with Percy as the high point of their son's life and asked Bob to scatter Peter's ashes on the sea after cremation. Bob agreed, and about four weeks later, in the company of one of his close friends, Dr Eric Ward, who also had a great love of dolphins, he set out in his inflatable from Portreath, taking a casket containing the ashes of Peter Worswick.

Bob solemnly read a poem written especially for the occasion by Canon Jerry Harper before casting Peter's remains on to the water at the precise spot where he enjoyed the happiest moments of his life – when he made direct contact with a free-ranging sea spirit.

Since Judy told me this tragic story I have reread some of Peter's letters. Now, after the experiences I am about to relate in this book, the anguish in Peter's ultra-sensitive mind when he discovered he had lost his beloved dolphins, is very clear to me.

This book is dedicated to the memory of Peter Worswick and Vincent van Gogh, two men who took their own lives because for them, the world was just too cruel a place in which to live.

I

Bill's First Encounter

For some people, touching a wild dolphin in the open sea is a vision they carry around in their minds. It is the ultimate cherished experience that most of them never have. For a handful of others direct contact with a wild dolphin just happens by chance, and Bill Bowell is one of these.

Swimming with a dolphin was something to which Bill had not given the slightest thought until September 1985 when, out of the blue, the magic moment came. At that time he was suffering from depression, and had done so for eleven years, living in what he described as a black pit of despair. On the day he met the dolphin a pin-prick of light appeared in Bill's darkness.

The events leading to Bill's depression repeatedly flashed through the darkened hall of his mind like a horror movie that he could not switch off. The film opens in Oxford in 1974. Bill lives happily in the city of dreaming spires with his wife Edna and their five children, until he has a heart attack. After a swift recovery he returns to his job managing a restaurant. Bill is a simple, honest and sensitive man whose loyalty to his employers outweighs his doctor's advice not to work too hard. When some money goes missing from the safe, Bill calls in the police and gives them every assistance. The next day two detectives visit him again. He is delighted when they tell him they have a suspect, but is dumbfounded when he himself is charged with the crime. In front of his staff, he is marched out ignominiously between two policemen and driven to the local police station. Desperately he pleads his innocence. Requests to telephone his wife and a solicitor friend are refused. His tie and shoelaces are removed and he is bundled roughly into a cell. The door clangs shut. The bolts are slammed home. Bill cracks. His mind is more damaged than if he had been whacked on the head with a truncheon. The prospect of losing his freedom is more than he can bear. He shouts out that he is innocent. He smashes his head against the cell wall, crumples to the floor and sobs. Several hours later the door opens and he is told that if he signs a piece of paper he can go. Exhausted, confused and totally bemused, he does what is asked of him. Bill then staggers out and heads for the river to drown himself. A friend, who knows that he has had a heart attack spots him, stops in his car and offers to take him home.

The screen goes black. The movie is over.

The four or five weeks following Bill's arrest no longer exist for him. Nature has wiped away that part of his memory. He has since filled in the space with pieces of information supplied by other people.

During his month out of contact with the world Bill became a zombie. He would neither eat nor utter a word, despite the love and support of his devoted family and assurances of their belief in his innocence. He lost weight. Slowly he was dying. Edna cooked his favourite meals and begged him to eat. Not until she told him that if he was going to starve himself to death then she too would die did he show any sign that he was conscious of anything around him. He took a few mouthfuls of food, and Edna's hopes for her husband's recovery began.

At times like these it is as well we cannot see into the future. For had Edna known just how long and painful Bill's return to anything like normality would be, she might have been overwhelmed. But as 1975 dawned she was hopeful and trusted that with her love and the wonders of modern medical care Bill would recover. Yet, despite examinations by specialists, chemotherapy, counselling and periods in psychiatric wards, Bill did not recover. He was classified as an invalid and unfit for normal work. Even when Bill was exonerated and the real thief identified, his depression did not lift.

A recurrent problem was agoraphobia. Sometimes Bill felt so unsure of himself that he would not leave the security of his modest terraced house. Edna helped him to overcome his fear of open spaces. First she would take him to the front door, and together they would progress to the gate. Then, on successive days, she would escort him further down the street until eventually he could pluck up enough self-confidence to go out and fetch himself a newspaper, or some tobacco.

Locked away in his own dark world, Bill was protected to some extent from what was going on around him. He was not conscious of the immense burden Edna was carrying. She was a quiet, reserved person and it was she who had to endure the looks of suspicious neighbours and withstand the ordeal of a court case during which the name of Bowell, her name, was splashed across the newspapers. With no savings and no income, she was dependent upon welfare benefits to feed and clothe herself, her invalid husband and their five children ranging in age from four to seventeen. She could not discuss and share the inevitable problems of parenthood and running a household with her husband. Nor did she attempt to do so, for fear of the effect the additional stress might have upon Bill.

Not until the children grew up and went out to work could the family afford to go away on holiday together. The tiny fishing village of Solva in Pembrokeshire, in the south-west corner of Wales, sounded like the peaceful haven they were looking for. They found a holiday cottage at a price they could just afford. It had the all-important feature of self-catering, which meant that Bill would not have to mix with people outside the family unless he wanted to do so.

Their vacation in Solva in 1984, the Bowells' first family holiday for seventeen years, was so successful that they decided to return in 1985. During the second visit Bill became more confident. He did not normally like crowded places, but halfway through their holiday the family persuaded him that he would enjoy a drink in the convivial atmosphere of the Harbour House Hotel – and that was where I first met him, quite by chance. It was the night I had offered to put on a film show, mainly for the locals, but also for any of the hotel guests who wished to come. Bill and his family were in the audience.

At the end of my presentation I mentioned the uplifting effect of dolphins on the human spirit, and how several people who had suffered nervous breakdowns appeared to benefit from contact with them. I couldn't explain it. I just reported what I had seen and been told.

I showed part of the film *Ride a Wild Dolphin*, which I had made with Barry Cockcroft in his 'Once in a Lifetime' series for Yorkshire Television in 1976. It concerned the antics of a dolphin called Donald, whose remarkable odyssey from the Isle of Man, to Ireland, to Wales and then to Cornwall I had followed and recounted in my books *Follow a Wild Dolphin* and *Save the Dolphins*. In the first I told the story of Geoff Bold, whose life was transformed when he met the dolphin Donald. Geoff described to me the circumstances that took him from London to Cornwall where he hoped he would find peace of mind. From talking to him it was clear that he had been close to a nervous breakdown. What stopped it happening was the dolphin Donald, who often spent hours playing with the breasting buoys just off the lifeboat slipway. Geoff told me that even when he was working on the lifeboat, inside the lifeboat station, he could detect the dolphin's presence outside, and that any anxiety he felt would evaporate when Donald arrived. This was one of the many tributaries I followed, at the time, in my quest for the source of the joyous spirit of the dolphin.

During the years that followed more and more evidence accumulated in my files. By 1985 I felt sure that contact with a wild dolphin could have a beneficial effect on depressives, and unlike most other treatments, I could not see it having any harmful side-effects. All the same, I had never put my theory to the test.

That situation changed after my show in the Harbour House Hotel when I was approached by Bill's daughter Karen who wanted me to take her father out to see the local dolphin with which I had made contact. There seemed no reason why I should not go along with her request. So I agreed.

It turned out to be one of those impulsive decisions that have far-reaching effects, in this case not just for Bill, but for countless others as well. In the laconic notes I scribble on such occasions I summed up next day, 12 September 1985, as follows: *a special day, a grey day, but a very happy day with dolphin sun shining thro'*.

I had not seen Bill in the audience, but when he singled himself out on the jetty the next day I noticed the haunted look, common in depressives, of not being quite in touch with reality. Edna, who had endured so much, was also quiet. For her husband's benefit she maintained an outward appearance of calm and gentleness. Unlike Bill, Edna could not swim, and was terrified of water, yet she displayed not the slightest trace of the fear she felt inside.

We scrambled into the large inflatable boat which was to take us through the harbour entrance to the open sea. There we hoped to make contact with the dolphin, or more accurately, it would make contact with us. I knew from experience, as did Chris, the skipper of the boat, that if the dolphin did not want our company it could outpace our engine and speed away from us in seconds.

We knew, however, that this was no ordinary dolphin. It was indeed one of those rare dolphins which, for reasons known only to itself, liked humans for company in the sea. But how could a dolphin looking for human company know we were around, especially if we were several miles apart? We had a secret weapon for letting it know our whereabouts – the outboard motor. Sounds travel great distances under water and we knew the dolphin could detect the noise of the engine from a long way off. Furthermore the dolphin was familiar with the sound, and seemed to know from previous encounters that those on board wanted to play.

At any rate, that was the theory. And it worked. Not immediately, but after we had cleared the foam-fringed rock that guarded the harbour entrance, revved the engine, and circled a couple of times in the open sea. Everyone cheered when the dolphin suddenly surfaced alongside us and then swam excitedly around the inflatable. Chris talked to the dolphin as if it were a friend before setting a course across the choppy water towards a natural rock archway, which we called Cathedral Rock.

In the boat were Richard Oldfield, known as Ric to his friends, but Rico to those who smiled at his cartoons in the journal *Diver*. He was accompanied by his diving buddy, Christine Williams. Both were experienced underwater swimmers, in contrast to the other member of the diving group Tricia Kirkman, who was a novice. Tricia had been working with me for three months on a film about the dolphin, but so far had never managed to dive without the intrusive presence of an underwater cameraman. Our plan that day was for all of us to go diving – with or without a dolphin escort – while Christine took Tricia on her first proper underwater tour.

The plan was working out well, and the dolphin followed us to Cathedral Rock. I knew only too well that we might lose its company at any time if an alternative source of amusement took its fancy. The dolphin wanted and expected plenty of action, and wanted it immediately. It would swim round the boat, urging us to get a move on. Anyone who knows anything about divers will know how long it can take them to get ready – especially if they are photographers too. First, there are all the items of diving equipment to be checked, adjusted and then double checked. Next comes the setting up of flashes and remote camera controls that have an irritating habit of failing just before the diver jumps into the water. The ritual of preparing for a dive, which Luciano, my long-term Italian diving friend, called his 'count down', often seemed to me to take ages. To an impatient dolphin it must have been interminable.

Fortunately, when we arrived near the archway Simo found a source of amusement close by. It was a seal. While our diving count down got under way, we watched as the two of them played together. First the seal's dog-like head appeared, its large gleaming eyes following the approaching dorsal fin. The dolphin circled slowly, watched continuously by the seal. Then the dolphin arched its back and there was a great flurry on the surface. A second later they had both disappeared.

Having spent many hours observing sea-lions in the Galapagos Islands, I knew how agile the seal family can be underwater – more than a match for dolphins in this respect. As I changed into my wetsuit, I imagined the two of them zooming like torpedoes along rocky canyons and tearing through the kelp in a game of tag. The seal, nervous of our presence, moved away from us, but the dolphin decided to double back and see how we were getting on. Its head reared out of the water and it looked into the boat at Tricia and me struggling to force shivering, lily-skinned limbs into our cold wetsuits, still damp and sticky from previous immersions in the sea. Usually, such situations resulted in a rush from the skipper, or other males standing by, to help Tricia, while I was left to struggle as best I could on my own. Neither of us was blessed with anything like a surfeit of muscle or adipose tissue – in a nutshell we were skinny.

The sight of my mini-biceps flexing as I fight my way into a wetsuit has often caused me some amusement. I wondered just how much the almost farcical scene of us divers getting kitted-up registered with the dolphin during the brief period in which its head was above water, looking into the boat. With that superb physical prowess and super-efficient insulation, the dolphin has no need to resort to the technology essential to our survival.

Chris and Ric didn't have the same problems when it came to getting dressed to go diving. They wore drysuits, which were baggy and relatively easy to get into. Except, that is, for the neck and wrist seals, which hermetically sealed them into their air-filled cocoons. Their problems came later when they were in the sea and wanted a pee.

Bill took little notice of us and said nothing while all this was going on. The dolphin had remained the centre of his attention from the moment he sighted it. As soon as the seal disappeared Bill started calling the dolphin, and when it reared up to look into the boat they made eye-to-eye contact. For the first time,

Bill broke his silence and spoke to Simo as if he were talking to a friend. When the dolphin submerged, Bill spontaneously picked up a piece of plastic hose and swept it back and forth through the water. Good, I thought, this is just what the dolphin needs. Fascinated by Bill's antics, the dolphin stayed close by the inflatable while Bill became steadily more vocal and oblivious to our presence.

Finally we were ready. Christine went in first to receive Tricia, who then lowered herself gingerly into the sea. The cold always took her breath away. As Tricia descended a small amount of water trickled into her mask, but she ignored it, entranced by what she saw as she swam down into what she later called 'a giant jewel box'. Part of the sea-bed and many of the kelp stipes were encrusted with small mussels. Starfish, spaced as randomly as the stars in the heavens and appearing almost as numerous, decorated the rock walls, which in places were stippled with what I call Daisy anemones, because of their bright yellow bodies and white tentacles. Every available space on the rock walls was occupied. Purple sponges competed for bedrock accommodation with Dahlia anemones of many different shades of purple and soft Alacionian corals. These are commonly known as Dead Men's Fingers, yet under water they resemble nothing like their name. Their thick stems are covered with what look like rosettes of tiny flowers in delicate shades of cream and pale orange. These are not petals but tiny tentacles that filter microscopic food particles from the broth of sea water in which they are bathed continuously. If they are removed from the water, the feeding tentacles retract instantly. The body contracts on to a rather unattractive stump, and it is easy then to see how the name arose.

Like a child let loose in Aladdin's Cave, Tricia did not know which way to turn. She swam from place to place, excitedly pointing out one thing after another as they took her attention. A small dogfish nestled on the top of a rock. Tricia stroked it gently under the chin and followed it when eventually it took off with lazy strokes of its tail. Time lost all meaning. If Christine had not kept an eye on the gauge, Tricia's air supply would have run out while she was still cruising among the giant boulders on the sea-bed. When the needle touched the red zone, Christine directed Tricia to start her ascent. Side by side, they soared upwards towards the rock arch which was mistily outlined above them, like an enormous cathedral window through which poured a green luminous light that became brighter and brighter as they approached the surface. Then their heads broke through the interface and they were once again back in a world of air, and rock-hard reality.

Divers cannot speak to one another under water and throughout her submarine excursion Tricia could use only gestures to communicate her excitement – which was obvious to anyone who could see her. When she was back in the boat the words that she had had to contain exploded like popcorn. She was wide-eyed with the wonder of it all. She was entranced by a crab she had seen reposing quietly in a crevice in the rocks. Seeing crabs and lobsters for the first time, alive and roaming in their own jewelled kingdom, she could not understand how anyone could remove, kill, and eat them.

I had seen a hundred times what Tricia was describing so excitedly. Her reaction to it was like that of a blind woman regaining sight and finding herself in a meadow full of flowers. It made me realise once more how fortunate I was, and that I should never take for granted the privilege of being able to descend into the alien world of the dolphin, which in many respects was as hostile as outer space, though infinitely more beautiful.

The passenger we had left on the boat was in his own reverie. Bill had stroked the dolphin's head, and there was no doubt that already a bond was being forged between them. The question was, could it be made even stronger by Bill getting into the water with the dolphin? There was one way to find out.

I had packed an old wetsuit into my diving bag. Bill wasn't a small man, and my chest has about the same circumference as the thigh of the average Sumo wrestler. Fortunately neoprene suits stretch, and we managed to squeeze him into the long-johns, although zipping up the jacket was impossible. Having

insulated Bill as best we could, we let him flop into the water
while holding on to one of the hand-lines on the inflatable. If he
felt the impact of the cold water, which I doubt, he showed no
sign of it. He lay motionless, spread-eagled on the surface
looking down into the dark mysterious depths.

Although a facemask enables the wearer to see clearly
under water, it limits the view to tunnel vision. Bill could see
the dolphin only when it was immediately in front of him.
Never having snorkelled or worn a wetsuit before, Bill, quite
naturally, was apprehensive, especially when he could feel
himself being bumped. He was unable to see anything going
on around his legs or midriff.

From the boat, however, we were able to observe exactly
what happened all the time Bill was in the water.

It started with the dolphin swimming up to him from behind
and then carrying out a complete examination. Having given
the fins a small nip with its teeth, the dolphin gently nuzzled
Bill's legs. Then it prodded Bill's body with its beak. Finally,
when the two of them were head to head, the dolphin poked
Bill so hard in the face that his mask nearly came off and he had
to shove the mouthpiece of his snorkel back into position.
Bill was not at all intimidated by what happened. Once he had
got the mouthpiece back he began to murmur words to the
dolphin through the tube, while observing for the first time
what the dolphin was doing, and more importantly seeing the
expression in its eyes.

From the boat it looked as if the dolphin was putting Bill
through a trial. When it was over, the dolphin's body language
showed it was jubilant with the outcome; accelerating away
from Bill at full speed, it swam in a tight circle, came back
and stopped abruptly in such a position that Bill's outstretched
arm rested on his neck. From that moment on any remaining
barriers between the two of them were gone. They became
locked together physically and mentally in such a way as I
had never before witnessed between man and dolphin after so
short an acquaintance. The dolphin rolled on to its back,
flippers in the air, while Bill stroked the smooth white belly.

As the moments flicked by the two mammals in the water became progressively less inhibited until they reached a stage when they were behaving like two old pals stepping, slightly unsteadily, out of the pub together – happy and oblivious to what the rest of the world did, or thought about them.

The rest of the world, however, was certainly not unaware of their antics. From the boat Edna saw traces of the Bill she knew and loved before 1974. For the first time she felt a lightening of the burden of responsibility she had been carrying so quietly, for so long. As she watched Bill and Simo together in the water she broke down and cried.

Tricia, ultra-sensitive as always, knew what was happening to Bill, and tears of joy ran down her cheeks too. She went over to Edna and gave her a hug. There was a bond between the two women as well as between Bill and the dolphin. For Tricia had had more than her fair share of hardship and despair while bringing up three children on her own. She told Edna how her life had been transformed since first meeting a dolphin. She also told Edna that when Bill came out of the water he too would bring with him some of the joy that dolphins share with all humans, especially those in need, like Bill.

· 2 ·

Operation Sunflower

The next day I climbed to the top of a hill and looked across Solva Harbour to the jetty opposite. A small cluster of figures was gathered on the slipway. I peered at them through my binoculars. One of them was Bill. Like the others, he was climbing into Jan Sendall's small fishing boat, the *Iolanthe*.

Tricia Kirkman, kitted up in her bright red wetsuit, was already on board. I saw her give Bill a hug when he stepped down on to the deck. A few minutes later the boat was heading out towards the open sea.

When the *Iolanthe* returned about two hours later I was waiting on the quay to meet it. I wanted to know how they had got on. Jan came alongside with his usual precision – the *Iolanthe* making a barely perceptible bump as it touched the wall. He held the boat tight to the harbour wall as I helped some of the passengers ashore. They were all excited and chatting about the dolphin. Tricia and Bill were the last to disembark. Tricia had spent over an hour in the sea with the dolphin and was radiant. Bill had not got into the water, but he had enjoyed every second he spent watching Tricia and Simo swimming and playing together. He was certainly not radiant – but the shadow that usually hung like a low cloud on his brow had lifted, and his face broke into a brief smile. Those few moments were very significant, for people suffering from depression do not smile.

I stood talking to Jan as Bill and Edna headed back to base, slowly making their way past the sailing dinghies at the top of the slipway. Bill was more relaxed than he had ever been since the traumatic events of 1974.

I picked up Tricia's holdall containing her fins, mask, snorkel tube and towel and together we strolled along the quayside behind Bill and Edna. Tricia, still wearing her bright red wetsuit and not exactly unnoticeable herself, commented that Bill was looking like a sunflower in his yellow oilskins. Then she remarked, 'You know Horace, since meeting the dolphin Bill has blossomed like a sunflower. Wouldn't it be wonderful if we could take lots more Bills out to see dolphins?'

The excitement of swimming with the dolphin has gone to her head, I thought. Why should I want to take a whole troop of Bills out to see dolphins in preference to, say, the girls from the chorus line at the London Palladium?

Tricia was serious, however, and her remark made me stop and think.

Ever since 1975, when I had watched and filmed Donald the dolphin in Cornwall, I had been aware that dolphins had an uplifting effect on the human spirit. Now, right in front of me, was living proof that they did more than this. Dolphins could actually help lift the debilitating burden from depressives. Nervous breakdowns, however, affect not only those who suffer them but also those close to them. Watching Bill and Edna walking side by side, on their way back to their holiday home and waiting family made me realise how much happiness the dolphin was bringing to people who really needed it. Like the yellow glow that radiates from a sunflower or a buttercup when the sun falls on it, the joyous energy of the dolphin was spreading to those nearest and dearest to Bill.

Okay, so spending time cavorting with a dolphin gave me great pleasure. But I was one of those people upon whom life had already bestowed more than its fair share of wealth – good health, a wonderful family, the freedom to travel, and to enjoy a lifestyle open to few. I didn't feel at all guilty about my lot. On the other hand, there was no reason at all why I shouldn't help others less fortunate than myself. Especially those for whom society, of which I was a part, created such pressures that they involuntarily withdrew, retreating into deep, dark holes which excluded them from the good things in life as well as the bad. I agreed with Tricia that, in principle, it certainly would be nice to think we could help many more people like Bill by taking them out to see dolphins. Yet the desire to do something immediately posed a question: how?

As it happened this was an area in which I had some expertise. Just before my first meeting with the wild dolphin Donald in 1974 I had spent a decade doing medical and veterinary research on a wide range of projects for a large pharmaceutical company. These included studying the effects of morphine-like drugs on many different animals, ranging from elephants to mice, and also evaluating the potential use these and other substances had in alleviating suffering in humans. I became well-versed in the procedures for running what were called 'double-blind cross over trials', designed to eliminate the placebo effect when assessing the efficacy of new drugs and formulations. Investigating dolphin influence posed new problems altogether.

'If we are going to do it at all, we will have to give the project a name and work out a plan of campaign,' I said impulsively. 'How about Operation Sunflower?'

One of the great advantages of being the Honorary Director of International Dolphin Watch and running it autonomously is that there is no need for committee meetings to make decisions.

'I will make Operation Sunflower the next major project for International Dolphin Watch,' I continued authoritatively.

Already the sunflower as a symbol was growing in my mind; not just because of Tricia's reference to Bill's blossoming like a sunflower but also because of the role sunflowers had played in the life of a man who lived a century ago.

Van Gogh was a painter whose work I much admired. What he did changed the world in a way which nobody at the time would have conceived as remotely possible. Even today few people realise how much he contributed to the way in which subconsciously we view our fellows and appreciate the components that make up the beauty of the things we see all around us, especially the landscape. Yet he endured the contempt of his contemporaries, producing hundreds of canvasses only one of which was sold in his lifetime, just before he died. None-the-less, such was his obsession that he continued his attempts to show the world what he could see and they could not.

The year 1888 started out as the most hopeful in Van Gogh's life. He moved to Arles in the south of France, where he rented a four-roomed property which was to be his 'House of Friends'. He painted it yellow and adorned it with six paintings of sunflowers. For him, yellow was the colour of the sun, a symbol of warmth, light and ecstasy.

In his year in Arles he worked with immense speed and produced some of his best work. For a while he was joined by Gauguin, whom he greatly admired, and their time together was electric, sometimes stormy. During a nervous breakdown van Gogh cut off his ear, and was admitted to hospital. As serenity slowly returned, he wrote: 'perhaps it is from the sick that one learns how to live.'

Between bouts of depression he was inspired to paint, but self-doubt grew inside him like a malignant cancer. In May 1889 he wrote, 'As a painter I shall never amount to anything, I am absolutely sure of it.' On 27 July 1890, he shot himself in the stomach. Two days later Vincent van Gogh died at the age of thirty-seven, just ten years after deciding to become an artist.

His sister said of him that, when he was a boy, he understood the 'souls' of flowers. To me, the essence of his paintings are not that they are representations of what he saw, but images of the intense passion that burned within him. When he looked at a sunflower he somehow *experienced* the sunflower. It is the undiluted and unashamed love radiating from his pictures a century after he painted them that I find so compelling.

Just as it was van Gogh who opened my eyes to the inner beauty of sunflowers, so it was Tricia Kirkman who first made me conscious of the fact that dolphins radiated what she called 'pure love'.

That particular moment of enlightenment took place in 1984. I had taken Tricia, who had never been in a swimming pool let alone in the sea, out to visit Percy, another dolphin I had befriended off the coast of Cornwall. Such was the compulsion she felt towards the dolphin that she overcame all her fears, put on a thin wetsuit and lowered herself over the side of the inflatable into the sea. The cold water snatched her breath away. When she moved away from the boat, just floating on the sea and quivering with terror, the dolphin came slowly up underneath her and let her rest her hands on his back. Then gently he towed her around the boat. It was one of those cameos in life that I shall never forget. I slipped into the water and took a picture of a lady, soon to become a grandmother, who couldn't swim, being given a ride by a wild dolphin on the first occasion she had been in the sea. A short time afterwards, while she was sitting on the side of the inflatable with her legs dangling in the water, the dolphin reared out of the sea and put its head on her lap. She bent down and kissed him.

Later, when I asked Tricia what the experience meant to her, tears streamed from her eyes. As briefly she relived the moment she said she felt pure love coming from the dolphin, which he gave her because of what was inside her, and bore no relationship to her sex, size, colour, shape or appearance.

When Tricia said that, she opened a window into the world of dolphin psyche for me. Yet it was not until I was holding my beautiful ten-month-old grand-daughter that I came close to comprehending why it was that dolphins have such a powerful effect on some people, especially those like Bill. It was a combination of the trust, innocence, gentleness and love that I shared with my grand-daughter, and that was the essence also of my personal relationships with wild dolphins.

Was this the pointer I needed to heed? If complex clinical trials were beyond my means, maybe I should try a different approach to the sunflower project. Instead of slavishly following some predetermined plan, why not trust my intuition?

· 3 ·

The Dolphins Take Over

I spent a long time pondering ways and means of bringing more depressives into direct contact with dolphins. Tricia was anxious to see that the seed she had sown did not perish for want of a little watering. She urged me on with assurances about my qualification, as a Fellow of the Royal Society of Medicine, and the need for a multi-discipline approach which she saw amply reflected in the thirty-odd papers I had published in various branches of scientific literature.

I felt less sure of my ground. It was true that I had never thought of biology, maths and physics as occupying separate compartments. When I left school I joined a team investigating the relationship of chemical structure to pharmacological activity in a range of drugs known as ganglion blocking agents. It was a mechanistic approach to the treatment of illness based on the premise that virtually all bodily activities are regulated by chemical reactions at a cellular level. By artificially modifying these biochemical processes with drugs, functions such as blood pressure could be brought under control. What I was attempting now with dolphins was anything but mechanical. Was it too fluid to be called 'scientific investigation' at all?

After graduating in Chemistry at London University I joined the Isotope Division of the Atomic Energy Authority at Harwell, where one of my research projects (for which I was awarded a Ph.D.) involved the use of radiotraces to investigate the mechanisms of complex heterocyclic chemical reactions. To expand my work on the peaceful uses of radioisotopes, especially in medicine, I further extended my studies into the biological sciences and physics. I could certainly mix disciplines but was it right to play around with people who were mentally sick?

Ever since my school days, when science first became an integral part of the world in which I lived, it diffused the boundary between work and play. While making a living in atomic research I brought up a family and took up diving as a hobby. I qualified as a First Class Diver in the newly-formed British Sub-Aqua Club. I also had a passion for photography and looked into some of the problems that arose when taking cameras into the sea. I published a book, *Camera Underwater*, which remained the standard work on the subject in Britain for more than a decade. I also founded the Oxford Underwater Research Group and led a scientific diving team to explore the geology of a pinnacle of rock known as East Rutts off the Devon coast. We published our findings in the journal *Nature*, and the film we made for BBC Television, *Neptune's Needle*, won awards at the Brighton Underwater Film Festival in 1967.

My interest in dolphins grew from the discovery that they had evolved from land animals millions of years ago. Just how amazing this evolutionary process had been was brought home to me when I tried wearing a pair of corduroy trousers and a woollen sweater to keep out the cold on my first dips into the sea. Emerging blue with cold and covered in dye from the trousers I realised how superbly insulated dolphins were. With a flexible layer of blubber the dolphins managed to retain what was arguably the most important feature of an earlier transition from reptile to mammal – that of maintaining a constant internal body temperature of about 38°C. Unlike the seals, dolphins even gave birth under water, producing offspring that suckled on extremely rich milk and were destined to spend their entire lives in waters often far colder than the sea in which I immersed myself for brief periods in the height of summer off the Devon and Dorset coasts. In a later book, *The Great Diving Adventure*, I recounted the sometimes hilarious outcome of attempting to encapsulate my body in a variety of home-made rubber suits in my desperate endeavours to emulate the dolphins and stay warm under water.

The often dismal and disappointing results I obtained when I took my cameras into the sea presented a challenge that led into the field of optics. When I put my head under water everything looked blurred. I had to use a facemask in order to see clearly. Yet, without any such device, dolphins appeared to be able to see equally well above and below the surface. They could also hurtle through the water at amazing speeds in zero visibility without bumping into things. I followed the work of pioneers like W. N. Kellog in the United States, who published a series of papers on how dolphins used their extraordinary sonar, which was far superior in many respects to anything scientists had managed to devise.

The evolutionary processes which transformed a four-legged land mammal into a dolphin resulted in an animal that was roughly fish-shaped. Unlike the fishes, however, the dolphin's tail moves up and down, rather than from side to side. When I put on a pair of rubber fins to propel myself through the water, the conversion of muscle energy into propulsive force was pathetically inefficient. Compared to a dolphin, I moved more like a snail than a greyhound.

I wondered how I could apply dolphin adaptations to my own performance. A German scientist, Dr Max Kramer, noted that dolphins experienced only 10 per cent the expected drag when they moved through water. This was due to their ability to eliminate turbulence in the water that flowed over their bodies. A dolphin's skin is connected to its body by interlocking protrusions called papillae, which enable the outer layer to move without wrinkling. When Dr Kramer set out to reproduce this effect artificially, he came up with the idea of attaching a rubber coating supported by a multitude of tiny pillars through which oil freely flowed to the surfaces of submerged hulls. His experiment resulted in a 50 per cent reduction in drag with a test object towed through the water. On the basis of this one result, it was argued in the journal *Industrial and Engineering Chemistry* in 1960, that successful application of the synthetic dolphin skin could lead to existing submarines travelling at 60 knots, and 'improved power plants could propel underwater craft at speeds of 210 miles per hour (180 knots)'.

When I began investigating methods that would enable divers safely to go deeper, and stay down longer, I also looked to the dolphins for inspiration. They are not susceptible to the bends and nitrogen narcosis which limited the depth and duration of human dives. Research showed that dolphins were extremely economical in the use of oxygen taken into their lungs through blowholes that opened for only a fraction of a second when they surface to breathe. In a paper published in *Nature* in 1966, a group of researchers at the Scripps Institution of Oceanography in San Diego reported that the heart rate of a dolphin was lowered from about 75 beats per minute on the surface to little more than 20 beats when it dived. This supported the view that during deep dives blood flow in the viscera and skeletal muscle was diminished, and that the limited supply of oxygen was reserved for the brain and other internal organs, such as the heart, where the maintenance of a high metabolic rate was so essential. Oxygen debts which would have a lethal effect in land mammals did not seem to disable dolphins, nor did levels of carbon dioxide in the blood, which would have caused humans to gasp for breath and lose consciousness.

Of all the research reports on dolphins it was the work of an American, Dr John Lilly, that especially caught my attention. He noted that weight for weight, a dolphin has a brain as large and also as complex as that of man. In his book, *The Mind of the Dolphin*, he disputed the notion that *Homo sapiens* alone was capable of speech, language, thought, feeling and imagination. He declared himself dedicated to the 'attempt to find means of communication between a human and non-human intelligence'. Lilly went so far as to suggest that an understanding of the dolphin's brain was the key to changing our misconceptions about the place of dolphins on the planet, and that a new ethic, with laws to support it, should evolve. He also proposed that future research should be designed to allow *voluntary* contacts between the two species.

In 1978, shortly after setting up International Dolphin Watch, I went to visit John Lilly and his late wife Toni at their home beside the Human Dolphin Foundation in California. During my stay I showed them the film I had made with Yorkshire Television about Donald, the dolphin off the coast of Cornwall, which demonstrated beyond doubt that it was possible to work with a free wild dolphin in the open sea. My approach was far less convenient and controlled than his because it required the researcher to go to the dolphin, once a willing dolphin was found. It also held the risk that a research programme could be disrupted at any time if the dolphin decided to swim away. All the same, I could guarantee that the dolphin's participation was altogether voluntary. Lilly was then working only with captive dolphins. He has since released them and vowed never again to capture dolphins for research purposes.

When I set up Operation Sunflower I accounted for my presence in Solva with Simo the dolphin, Bill the depressive and Tricia the super-sensory as simply the end of a long chain of strange incidents and coincidences. Yet four years later I could not escape the view that, meeting the dolphins in complete freedom, I had somehow allowed control to pass to them. The notion was to be reinforced through a series of mysterious happenings which I could not have foreseen when I started in Solva. The new concept was at odds with my training, which admitted only measurable, quantifiable and repeatable observations as valid data from which to draw inference. I was flirting with a hunch that was more mystical than scientific, and it put me in a dilemma. Would I have to throw over all my scientific background, or else abandon such fancies? I could do neither.

·4·

The Arrival of Simo

When starting work on Operation Sunflower I began in typically scientific fashion by attempting to find out as much as I could about the dolphin's previous history. It was first sighted by a canoeist in the week before Easter, 1984, near the wreck of two tugs in an area close to Solva known as The Cradle. Through May and June the dolphin made contact with local fishermen who reported it following their boats and closely watching the pots they hauled in. When the fishermen showed a friendly interest in the dolphin's presence, it became progressively bolder. Eventually the dolphin allowed the skipper of the *Vital Spark*, Willie Bach Phillips, to touch it with an oar.

As spring turned to summer, and boating activities increased, many helmsmen found unexpectedly a dolphin accompanying them when they sailed near the rusting hulks off The Cradle. When the sun-worshippers emerged from their winter hibernation the dolphin extended its territory to include Gwadn, where a sandy beach was exposed at low tide. It was a popular area for swimmers, visitors and locals alike, and the presence of a dolphin cruising along close to the shore added interest and excitement for those who ventured into the chilly water.

Divers found the dolphin even further afield, where it would swim skittishly round the wetsuited figures who flopped into its world close to the rocks at Porth y Bwch. It was the activities of three young locals – David Canby-Lewis, Carl Mason and Jonathan Tite – that attracted the dolphin more than anything else. David worked as a chef at the Harbour House Hotel, and during his time off in the afternoons he and his friends would zoom out in his small boat. When the weather was fine, calm and warm, they would anchor off the rocks in a secluded cove and frolic in the sea. Sometimes they put on masks and snorkelled down, flying over the green underwater forest of kelp and shooting between the rocks before returning to the surface to gasp for air. At other times they scrambled up the cliff face and dived off the rocks into the crystal waters. They were a happy, carefree trio who enjoyed their hours of freedom on, under and beside the sea. When the dolphin discovered them, he immediately picked up their devil-may-care spirit and joined in the fun, swimming alongside and getting very excited when they snorkelled down into the depths. The dolphin became more and more friendly as the idyllic summer days passed. By the beginning of August the dolphin was so much part of the group that it allowed them to touch it when they were all in the water together.

On Tuesday, 14 August 1984, David's parents, Margaret and Graeme Canby-Lewis, who owned and managed the Harbour House Hotel, took one of their rare and much treasured afternoons off in their boat the *Tic Tac*, and with them went Anne Marks, whose daughter Jenny was friendly with David. As the *Tic Tac* made its way with stately progress out of the harbour David sped past in his 'rock hopper', a very light aluminium-hulled boat that skimmed like a super-charged water beetle across the sea. His parents were anxious to meet the dolphin he had befriended.

Outside the harbour they turned westwards towards The Cradle. It was not long before David was speeding towards them with the dolphin riding his bow, sometimes leaping out of the water. David tied up to the stern of *Tic Tac* and he and Jenny jumped into the sea for a swim. The dolphin circled them, keeping just out of reach. Jenny's mother, Anne, could not resist the chance of swimming with the dolphin, and she too leapt into the sea and stayed in for half an hour. The weather was perfect. Early sea fog had cleared, there was no wind, the sea was flat calm and underwater visibility extremely good. Towards the end of their swim, the dolphin became quieter and more tame and allowed the two youngsters to brush it gently with their finger-tips when it swept past.

In Cornwall at this time I was enjoying a relationship with a wild dolphin which had reached an advanced stage. That dolphin's name was Percy, and on 3 September 1984 I had what was to be my very last encounter with him. I have relived it dozens of times because it was one of the high points in Laurie Emberson's television film, *Eye of a Dolphin*, which I show at some of my film presentations. Time and again on that day, the dolphin had leapt around me while I talked to camera of my heartfelt view that dolphins should never be kept captive in boxes. Percy made the point far more eloquently than ever I could by the sheer exuberance and joyfulness of his free-ranging aquatic acrobatics.

After the filming we adjourned to a quayside pub. With the dolphin's co-operation we had got better footage than we had ever dreamed possible.

That night Tricia Kirkman arrived at the Holborns' guest house, anxious to swim with Percy again. When she awoke the next morning, the sea was angry. Grey spume-topped waves were dumping themselves on the beach outside. After the long train journey her hopes were dashed.

It is an onshore wind that makes the sea rough close inshore. If the wind is blowing off the land, waves are pushed away from the coast and do not throw themselves on to the beaches or the rocks. I knew, therefore, that although the sea was rough off Portreath on the north coast, it would be much calmer off the south coast of Cornwall and the south coast of Wales.

'I've had a call from someone called Anne Marks,' I told Tricia when I saw her disappointment. 'She says there's a dolphin off the Pembrokeshire coast. Of course he won't be as friendly as Percy, and we might not get a sighting of him. But the weather should be calmer there, and I'm thinking of taking the car to Solva. Do you want to come along?'

Tricia did not hesitate, and some hours later we were settled in the Harbour House Hotel with Anne Marks, the Canby-Lewis family and a crowd of other people, all with dolphin stories to tell. The atmosphere was warm and friendly, with Margaret playing hostess.

To start with everyone referred to the dolphin as 'The Dolphin'. 'Haven't you given him a name?' I asked. They said they weren't sure of its sex. Then Anne suggested Simo, which avoided identifying the dolphin as either male or female.

Simo is actually a Greek word meaning snub-nose, and in ancient times it was a traditional nickname for dolphins. In recent years it has become associated with a single friendly dolphin as a result of the story-teller Pliny the Elder recording in AD 70 how the son of a poor fisherman living in Pozzuoli on the Bay of Naples was ferried to school across an inlet called Lake Lucrine on the head of a dolphin. The boy would summon his mount by calling, 'Simo, Simo', from the shore. This went on for several years until, quite suddenly, the child died. The dolphin continued to come to the shore and pined for the boy. When his former friend failed to appear, the dolphin was overcome by grief and died of a broken heart.

Pliny the Elder himself perished in an eruption of Vesuvius in AD 79. When the engulfed town of Pompeii was excavated centuries later, one of the many stylised wall paintings uncovered showed a young boy riding on a dolphin.

Cynics may say that Pliny was too free with poetic licence when accounting for Simo's sad end. But was it romantic anthropomorphism? I think not. For the events that were about to unfold in Solva would reveal that after an interval of some 1,900 years the bond between a human and a dolphin could grow into what can only be described as love. This time, however, the human involved was not a child but a parent.

After all the talk in the Harbour House Hotel I was anxious to see for myself just how strong the connection between the Solva dolphin and humans had become. I was assured there would be no difficulty in arranging a meeting. All the same, wild dolphins like to ensure that we don't get too complacent about the friendship they offer us, and Simo made this quite clear the following day.

I made an early start. Somehow or other, the media had got to know of my presence in Solva and I was pressed for a live interview with BBC Radio Wales shortly after 8 a.m. Within an hour Solva was seething with cameramen wanting pictures of the dolphin.

Solva is a natural harbour fed by a small river. Most of the moorings dry out at low water, and we had to wait until ten o'clock for the *Tic Tac* to come afloat. Then, with all our gear on board, and with Graeme Canby-Lewis as skipper, we set off along the channel out of the secluded harbour, turning west into a strong wind which rattled the halyards. David had gone ahead of us in his own boat to scout out the dolphin. When he failed to locate it, we decided to run from one end of the dolphin's territory to the other. There was no sign of the elusive Simo.

Eventually we anchored in a sheltered bay, said to be its favourite playground. There I tried every device I knew to attract the dolphin. I rattled the anchor chain over the side while David and his friends buzzed around in their little boats – but no dolphin appeared.

During the afternoon Maggie Canby-Lewis came out with a BBC cameraman in another boat and transferred to the *Tic Tac*. We sat in the sunshine, eating sandwiches Maggie had prepared. One of the youngsters climbed halfway up the cliffs and jumped off into the water – just for fun. Still no dolphin.

At length the photographers gave up and returned to Solva harbour. With the sun well over the yard-arm, Graeme broached the gin and we perched on the cabin roof with our drinks. A boatful of trippers came past. David went over to ask if they had seen the dolphin. He came rushing back to our mooring with news that it was in the next bay. Within seconds the anchor was up and we were off round the headland, David ahead of us, and it was not long before we saw the dolphin dancing on his bows. I put on my wetsuit and entered the water.

My first impressions of Simo were that he was a delightful youngster, not yet fully grown, and quite different to Percy in size and maturity. I estimated his length to be just under 2 metres; Percy had measured 3.8 metres. He had several very deep wounds on his dorsal fin which looked as if they might have been caused by a propeller. I say 'he' because I was able, quite positively, to determine his sex.

The dolphin came up to me almost immediately, and I put my arms around him. He rested his pectoral fins on my shoulders – a lovely gesture for our first encounter. I had sent my aqualung cylinder and weight-belt back on the boat carrying the cameramen, and so couldn't dive, but the four of us now in the water – David, Tricia, Anne and myself – enjoyed a great game of hide-and-seek with Simo round the reef where the *Tic Tac* was moored. He liked to be scratched, especially at the base of the pectoral fins.

Simo regurgitated a mass of what looked like fat Polo mints, together with other white bits and pieces that sank slowly. I tried to grab some but failed, and called over to David, who dived down and collected a couple of specimens for me. These were put into a glass of gin in the hope that the alcohol would preserve them for later analysis.

I was reluctant to leave, but if the *Tac Tac* didn't make it back to Solva before low water she would have to stay out for eight or nine hours. We changed into dry clothes and talked excitedly about our encounters with Simo. There was a feeling of jubilation on board as we sailed back across the bay past the point where we had spent a fruitless five hours waiting. We had been so near and yet so far from where the dolphin was playing.

Simo followed us round the headland to his old playground, where he left us and swam to the rocks. As we neared the harbour entrance we were surprised to see another boat coming towards us, with television crew and a freelance photographer on board. They had heard that the dolphin had made an appearance and rushed back to sea. I tossed my snorkelling gear on to their boat, quickly jumped across and was soon returning in the direction from which I had just come. We found Simo feeding along a reef. The dolphin rose to the surface several times in quick succession before making very deliberate diving movements. I donned my soggy wetsuit again. Simo took little notice of the boat as it circled him, and the camera crew got good pictures of the dolphin they had come for.

I jumped overboard. Simo immediately stopped feeding and swam towards me. To my surprise, I saw him approach with the remains of a mullet sticking out of his mouth. He darted round me, and it was only after several circuits that the tail of the fish finally disappeared down his gullet. It was lovely to be in the water with him. He obviously welcomed the opportunity to have another frolic – despite the fact that it took place right in the middle of his tea-time!

Presently I climbed back on the boat, where the television reporter asked me to sit on the stern and do an interview with him. The wind had dropped and the sun was setting as we cruised back to Solva. Everything had turned out perfectly in the end.

With sprigs of seaweed stuck jauntily in the top of one of my bootees I made my way to the Harbour House Hotel and thankfully discarded my rank wetsuit. It was a joy to get into a bath after being enveloped in sponge neoprene for so long. Divesting myself of the restricting wetsuit was psychologically like removing a swimming costume and swimming naked in the sea. It added to the blissful sensuality of wallowing in the warm, scented foam.

· 5 ·

Singing in the Rain

In 1984 Tommy Boyd, the presenter of ITV's *Saturday Show*, offered opportunities for selected young viewers to fulfil their dreams. Meeting a pop star ranked high on the list of requests, but by far the most numerous letters he received revealed longings to swim with a dolphin. This was a relatively easy wish to grant in dolphinariums eager for publicity. Tommy had once been a trainer at Brighton Dolphinarium but close contact with dolphins in captivity became so distressing for him that he had to leave. Like all dolphin trainers, he dearly loved the animals in his care and vowed never again to exploit them for entertainment. Yet the affinity he felt towards dolphins remained deeply rooted in him.

When the requests to swim with a dolphin came pouring in to his programme they nourished a dream that he too had nurtured since childhood – to swim with a dolphin free in the wide open sea. Through my filming partner, Chris Goosen, who had worked with Tommy on a whale film, I knew I could fulfil his dream and at the same time give a young viewer the experience of a lifetime.

Three weeks after my first meeting with Simo I was back in Pembrokeshire with an eight-year-old lad named Steven Walker, his youthful mother Joy and Tommy Boyd. We met for the first time in the railway station at Haverfordwest and I drove them to Solva. Tommy had brought two wetsuits with him, which Steven tried on during the evening (eventually wearing one over the other) before the young TV star-to-be went excitedly to bed.

The following morning we were aboard Jan Sendall's boat, *Iolanthe*, by 10.30 a.m. and turned to starboard outside the harbour, going to the outermost limit of Simo's territory . . . but no dolphin!

Jan said that never before had he failed to find Simo when he came out this far. Unspoken words rattled around in my head.

We decided to head east and explore the caves at Pendinas as far as the wrecks. As we approached we saw a dolphin bounding across the sea towards us. Tommy was so excited you would have thought it was the first time he had ever encountered a dolphin. Our paths came together in exactly the same place as my first meeting with Simo.

An explanation for the dolphin's earlier absence was apparent from a boat that could be seen disappearing over the horizon. Before we left the harbour it had gone out to sea though in a different direction from that taken by the *Iolanthe*. Simo had followed the other vessel and was well clear when we emerged from the harbour fifteen minutes later. The fact that the dolphin had deserted the other vessel to come and see us added to the sense of privilege we all felt at having Simo's company.

Contact, however, was short-lived. After getting us to rush repeatedly from one side of the boat to the other as he swam round us, drawing shrieks from those hanging over the side of the boat whenever he was spotted rising from the depths, Simo went off to feed.

I recognised the signs. When I saw the deliberate humping of the dorsal fin just before it disappeared beneath the surface, I knew I was watching the launch of a food-seeking missile that had already found its target by sonar, and having locked on, was rocketing after its prey. The power and speed with which Simo was chasing the fish could not be seen by those in the boat. Very little energy was wasted moving masses of water. All that was visible on the surface around the thrusting tail was a small, completely circular wave that rapidly spread outwards until its energy was spent. As the wave expanded it created a disc of flat water on the surface of the sea that lasted for only a few seconds before it was gone. By that time Simo was several hundred metres away, with a luckless fish clamped between his interlocking teeth. He surfaced triumphantly a quarter of a mile away, brandishing his silver prize to loud cheers from those on board.

Having demonstrated complete independence, Simo went on to turn upside down the master/servant relationship which prevails in dolphinariums between humans and dolphins. It soon became abundantly clear that he was the master and we humans the performers. To begin with, the food-reward system employed by dolphin trainers could not be used to persuade Simo to perform for us. On the contrary, he bribed us, by his presence, to perform for him. This reversal of roles came into being when I explained to those on board the *Iolanthe* that if we wanted to keep the dolphin's company we would have to entertain him with as many tricks as we could devise. Anne Marks produced a lanyard with a bronze clip that she used for training horses and trailed it in the water, letting it clink against the side of the boat. It was just the sort of sound she felt sure the dolphin would find interesting. Simo came over to inspect it for a few moments and then went away to play with some seals, leaving us with the distinct impression that we would have to do better than that!

It was a glorious day, warm and with only a little wind. The heavens seemed to sing with sunshine. I watched a mother seal as she in turn watched her pup clamber out on to a rock. A few moments later a wave swept the seal back into the sea. Then, just as children will develop games if left to their own devices, the young seal and the young dolphin began playing together. Several times the seal climbed on to the rock. When it was swept back into the water beside the waiting dolphin, a frantic chase would ensue, with both of them leaping out of the sea as they rushed along a gully. A couple of times the mother joined in, but she was always aware, and wary, of our presence. With dripping-wet white whiskers glistening in the sun, she watched us and her offspring with large luminous eyes, ready to whisk her baby away to safety in an instant if we made a threatening move or gesture.

It was little wonder that Simo showed only passing interest in the mechanical contraptions with which we had sought to entertain him. Humans swimming in the water, however, were a different matter – nowhere near as agile, nor as at home in the water as seals of course, but nevertheless worth inspection. As the humans kitted-up in wetsuits and went into the sea Simo came to play.

I filmed them from the boat. Eventually I put my old mechanical Bolex camera into its underwater housing and slid into the sea myself. Although the air was crystal clear, the water was murky, and Simo was never still for a second. With the dolphin zooming in and out of view I was able to get only fleeting shots of him passing by.

Children have an instinct for self-preservation that prevails at the last minute and protects them from taking unnecessary risks. Any bravado they may exhibit when associating with their peers vanishes when faced with an untimely departure from the world. Caution took a strong hold of young Steven when he was finally confronted with the prospect of leaping overboard into the ivory-lined jaws of a highly energetic and excitable dolphin considerably bigger than himself. Despite our assurances that he would come to no harm, Steven watched the cavorting dolphin with apprehension as we wrapped him in the two wetsuits. Both were several sizes too big. So loose were they that the water would be sure to come flooding in and I knew they would offer little thermal protection.

Now, even without the presence of a powerful wild animal, I have seen many adults in their prime quake at the prospect of launching themselves into the cold sea, so when Steven lowered himself down the ladder, I was not surprised to find him rebounding back into the boat the moment the icy water gripped his ankles. We told him, of course, that it was all in his mind, and that once he had got over the first shock he would feel as warm as toast. Cajoled by our reminders that the entire nation would watch the film I was shooting for television, he bravely descended again and pushed himself away from the ladder.

Unfortunately his physiology was not as co-operative as I predicted. Steven continued to shiver. This did not enhance our credibility in his eyes. The sight of a triangular fin rushing towards him, cutting a path through the water as smoothly and as swiftly as a surgeon's knife across a naked abdomen, also did nothing to reduce his shivering which, if anything, increased. To make matters worse, Steven's fins came off. He ended up with his arms around Tommy, like a baby chimpanzee clinging to its mother. This wasn't the climax to the film I had had in mind.

Tommy was marvellous, telling Steven how brave he was and how well he was doing – as indeed he was. I had spent weeks in my twenties learning to snorkel in a swimming pool before even thinking of going into the sea. With Tommy's encouragement he swam back to the boat while Simo cruised around near by.

When filming was finished for the day, other passengers on board went for a swim with the dolphin. Simo stayed near the boat until six o'clock. Then reluctantly we weighed anchor and headed back to harbour.

The next day we went out again, this time with an extra passenger, also a presenter of children's television programmes whose name was Sue Robbie. Young Steven, now rested and buoyed up by survival of his first ordeal, was now much more confident in the water. It was the cold more than anything that had worried him before. Tying off the bottom of the legs of his wetsuits meant that he couldn't wear fins but at least his breath wasn't taken away when he went in, and he happily dog-paddled in the water among the rest of us.

Even though the temperature doesn't change, the sea always *feels* warmer when the sun is shining. The soft golden light of autumn beamed down on to water unruffled by wind throughout the entire day. With the previous day's experience behind us the filming also went much more smoothly.

As Tommy left with his guests the following day, however,

the wind came howling through Solva, and an angry grey sky spat pellets of rain into their faces. Jan Sendall took his boat out for the few who remained. The wind was blowing directly off the sea, and it gathered up white horses that galloped across the heaving ocean into the harbour entrance as the ex-North Sea diver defiantly pointed the *Iolanthe* towards them, opened the throttle and charged. The bow of his boat reared out of the water, nosed down, and then rose again. I tried to film the spectacle but was thrown from one side to the other as soon as I let go of a hand-hold. Even with two people trying to hold me steady the movement of the boat was so violent that we all went crashing over. My camera was getting drenched with a mixture of rain and spume blown off the waves, the tops of which sometimes poured over the side and into the boat. After taking a few sequences I settled for enjoying the screaming wind, the stinging lash of the rain on my cheeks and a bucking bronco ride. Our cockle-shell of an open boat was dwarfed by the waves. As we rose and fell with the ragged rhythm of the sea I wondered what Simo the dolphin was experiencing. One thing was certain, his world would be full of tumultuous noise.

One of the pioneers of underwater exploration, Jacques Cousteau, described the sea as a silent world. To inhabitants of the ocean with acute hearing, like the dolphin, nothing could be further from reality. This was borne in on me when I listened-in to the sea with a sensitive underwater microphone on a calm day. It was like turning on the lights in a pitch dark room. In an instant I became aware of grains of sand striking one another, and that rolling pebbles produced clinks that flowed together like the notes in a musical score. To my new-found ears the amplified growl of a single wave progressing up a beach some distance away was just one of the ingredients in a whole symphony of natural sounds. There were other instrumentalists in the undersea orchestra. These included snapping shrimps and rasping lobsters that crackled like distant machine-gun fire. Swimming scallops added a softer 'clop, clop, clop,' to the percussion. The strings and wind sections were combined in waves that gurgled softly as they slid sinuously into and out of rocky gullies, rustling the half-exposed seaweeds as they flowed.

That was on a calm day. In a gale, in a small open boat, I could feel the fury of the storm, and I knew that such gentle passages of sound would be overwhelmed by the crashing cymbals of the sea hurling itself against the cliffs, the thunderous thumping of waves on a sandy beach and the hissing fury of a wavefront rushing along a rockface. Overlaid on this would be the howling wind. Indeed, the wind was the demented conductor of my imaginary undersea orchestra. It was the wind that moved the flat sea into valleys and hills. It was the wind that drove the waves over the water running back down the beach creating a wild turmoil of froth and foam. It was the wind that urged the sea to perform for us. And, on the morning in question, the ocean responded with a tumultuous and terrifying roar.

It is likely that the sound of our engine was lost in the continuous barrage of undersea sound, for we did not make contact with Simo during our brief but memorable excursion. We returned just in time for Jan to put the *Iolanthe* on her mooring before the harbour dried out.

We agreed to meet again on the jetty when the tide flooded in in the late afternoon. Among the group gathered on the quayside six hours later were Tricia Kirkman and her son Matthew. The wind had dropped, but the sky was still leaden grey. So too was the sea. Despite the gloom, Tricia was desperately keen to go out and see if we could find Simo. Jan Sendall was easily persuaded, and we sallied forth once more.

Outside the harbour entrance the sea had calmed, and it was not long before we had a dolphin for company. Despite the gathering dusk, Tricia was determined to swim with Simo. While the rest of us stayed on board she went into the water. Simo was delighted with the first human contact he had had all day and made his feelings perfectly clear to Tricia. He swam excitedly round her and reared his head high above the surface, imitating her upright posture in the water.

Both Jan and I were extremely experienced divers having

logged thousands of hours undersea between us. We both knew that the woman we had released into the sea was unable to swim, though buoyed up by her wetsuit, we also knew she couldn't sink. We watched her carefully and were prepared to haul her out instantly if the need arose. Even so, we were aware that it takes more than a modicum of courage for a non-swimmer to cast herself adrift, unaccompanied, in a heavy sea in the presence of a powerful, wild creature, albeit a dolphin.

Nobody loved Simo more than Jan Sendall, who was a quiet and reserved man with hidden strength. But as he watched Simo and Tricia playing in the water he knew that this was not just another of the many visitors he took out to see the dolphin. There was an immensely strong compulsion inside Tricia that overcame her fear and her sensitivity to the cold.

Seeing Simo and Tricia together in the gloom, it was obvious that a great affinity existed between the woman and the dolphin. What neither of us knew at the time, however, was that we were witnessing the formation of a bond that in the course of time would become intensely emotional.

It was dark when Tricia climbed up the ladder we had lowered over the stern of the *Iolanthe*. Hastily we raised anchor and headed back to base. Suddenly Simo performed an enormous leap, level with the top of the wheel-house. I am not sure if Tricia's shriek of delight frightened Simo or stimulated him, but he immediately made another fantastic acrobatic vault high in the air.

On the way back to harbour Tricia sat with her legs dangling on either side of the bow, bouncing up and down in the heavy swell. Simo's final salute had etched itself on her memory. She was in a state of ecstasy as the boat plunged through an extra large wave that tugged at her legs and smothered her with foam. Anyone seeing and hearing her from the shore might have assumed she had been drinking, though we all knew this was not the case. There was no doubt, however, that Tricia was completely intoxicated – by the dolphin.

I drove to London the following day and collected my wife Wendy, my mother and a great aunt from various stations and took them to the West End where we had seats booked for the Tommy Steele show 'Singing in the Rain' at the London Palladium. It was a wonderful spectacle which we all enjoyed, especially the rain sequence that had posed so many technical difficulties to set up.

As I sat in a warm comfortable seat, watching the dazzling colours, and listening to the familiar songs I could not help comparing my situation with that which I had been in the previous day. How fortunate I was to be able to enjoy two wonderful though completely different experiences with only one thing in common – they both left me with a warm afterglow, a feeling of pleasure which I wanted to talk about and share with others.

This casts an interesting light on the workings of the human mind. At times of special excitement, when the stimuli from the various sources impact on our bodies, they generate pulses that travel through the nervous system to different centres in the brain. Thus, through my eyes and ears, I would have registered the immediate individual sensation of the colours and sounds of the seascape at Solva and the show at the London Palladium. Selected signals would then be transmitted to the outer layer of my brain, the cerebral cortex.

A prerequisite for the enjoyment of music is the establishment of a network connecting the auditory cortex (where impulses are received directly from the ear via the auditory nerve) with other sections of the brain – especially the cerebral cortex. When everything is working well and smoothly, the sound of a familiar tune may induce a feeling of pleasure. The existence of our large cerebral cortex enables us to engage in aesthetic experiences at levels denied to those animals which lack the necessary brain structure. All the same, this supposed mental superiority can be a double-edged sword. For in addition to enabling us to experience the highs of great joy, our large cerebral cortex also endows us with an ability to experience the deep lows of depression.

Consider for a moment what happens when a succession of wrong notes are struck. Pulses running round the network take unexpected courses. In an instant pleasure can turn to irritation. This can lead to displeasure and even despondency. In terms of what is happening in the brain network, the immediate experiences of joy and melancholy are closely related.

People suffering from depression are often highly intelligent and very capable. Their problems arise from relatively few signals being switched on to the wrong circuits, which renders them incapable of enjoying the pleasure of the moment. This can give rise to long-term emotional difficulties which may be dismissed as trivial by more fortunate members of society not afflicted with prolonged bouts of the blues. Some people believe that depression can be remedied simply by 'pulling yourself together'. In fact, sufferers know that the inability to cope with the needs – real or imaginary – imposed by themselves and society can be utterly debilitating.

When their condition reaches an advanced stage, those suffering from anxiety and nervous breakdown can quickly be diagnosed. Yet some people who suffer from such mental illnesses manage to disguise or hide them. Certainly the sight and sound of Tricia Kirkman's unbounded ecstasy at meeting the dolphin might cause the casual observer to conclude that she hadn't a care in the world. But they would be wrong. Fearful dragons that could strike at any time lurked in the deep recesses of her past. For her, meeting the dolphin did more than just set the metaphorical train running on the right track in her head to give her an immediate sensation of pleasure. It also generated a feeling of euphoria that lasted long after her return to shore. This was due to release of biochemicals whose production is stimulated by the brain. She had no direct control over this process. During fits of depression, the secretion of the biologically active substances that gave her this ongoing feeling of joy and well-being were either not produced or were blocked at the site of their action in the brain.

When I set out to introduce Tommy Boyd and Steven to the dolphin in Solva, I had no idea where it would lead. I certainly did not imagine it being the prelude to an investigation of the role dolphins might play in helping humans suffering from depression. But that is what eventually happened.

It came about after I witnessed at first hand the intense relationship Tricia Kirkman developed with the dolphin. She had already told me how the dolphin gave her a feeling of being loved. As the ghosts of her past revealed themselves to me during random conversations I realised that, for Tricia, Simo satisfied a deep emotional need. Furthermore, it was one she shared with many other sensitive and vulnerable members of human society.

·6·

The Cave

The mysterious mind of the dolphin fascinated me and Simo's presence in Solva lured me to Pembrokeshire as irresistibly as the sirens called to the sailors in Homer's *Odyssey*. The providential appearance off the British coast of this friendly dolphin filled the vacuum left by Percy's sudden disappearance and enabled me to continue, without interruption, my exploration of the complex relationship between ourselves and the large-brained mammal so aptly dubbed by Robert Stenuit as man's cousin in the sea.

I had no idea how long Simo would stay around in Solva, or indeed whether he would still be there the following spring. Jan Sendall, the boatman, was very attached to Simo and promised to go out whenever he could to maintain contact during the winter months when human traffic in and out of Solva harbour would be at its lowest. There would be days, possibly even weeks, when the winter gales would completely close down boating operations. What would a dolphin, who had shunned the company of his own kind in preference for that of humans, do then? The question was unanswerable.

I had to assume that Simo would remain, and upon my return home I produced what in television circles is called a 'treatment' for a documentary film about the Welsh dolphin. Like a stray cat, the script of my proposed film wandered in and out of several television stations before it eventually found a sympathetic home at Harlech Television in Cardiff. The story I submitted involved retelling Tricia's experience with Percy, that of a non-swimmer going into the sea with a wild dolphin and then progressing from there to the stage where she would put on an aqualung and join the dolphin in his undersea world.

Before a contract was signed with HTV, Colin Stevens, the director whom I had met earlier in London wanted to see Simo and Tricia for himself. So it was that on 8 May 1985 Tricia and I arrived in Solva, and at 6 p.m. stood on the jetty amid a host of children who also wanted to see Simo.

Outside the harbour the sea was almost flat, and it wasn't long before the dolphin could be seen cutting a track across the waves towards us. The children grew very excited as Tricia and I changed into our brand new Beaver wetsuits. I jumped in while Tricia lowered herself gingerly down the ladder and into the water. The first shock took her breath away. She quickly became accustomed to her new aquatic environment, however, and was soon splashing around – much to the enjoyment of Simo who had followed us to an anchorage close to the shore. The dolphin came up to each of us in turn before disappearing. A few minutes later he was back. It was delightful to be with him again and to see that he had put on weight and was in excellent condition. He had many new marks on his body, but the deep wound on his dorsal fin which made him very easy to identify was healing well. Some of the scratches on him ran parallel to one another – Jan told us it was thought that these were the result of playing with a seal, or that they were made by the teeth of a Killer whale, or another large dolphin. From what I had seen of the dolphin's behaviour I thought the first the most likely explanation. I told Jan that this was not at all unusual – I had seen wild Bottlenose dolphins in many parts of the world and they were invariably extensively marked. The scars they bore were the results of the rumbustious lives they lead.

Visibility was around 3 metres. We stayed in the water for about an hour. Jan then moved back towards the harbour with Simo following behind the boat just below the exhaust pipe, effortlessly keeping up with us in his favourite position. The children hung over the stern watching as he trailed us right into the harbour. Having put some of the youngsters ashore, Jan took the boat out into the middle of the harbour again and Tricia went in for another swim with Simo. The dolphin had very distinct phases of going to the swimmer in the red wetsuit and then leaving her for a while. According to Jan, this was Simo's usual pattern of behaviour.

The next morning Colin Stevens joined us for breakfast, and we were on the jetty by 10.30, accompanied by a group of children and parents who wanted to go dolphin spotting. Just before we left the harbour a fishing boat departed in front of us. The sea was rough and there was a strong wind blowing. It was bright and sunny, however, and I scanned the horizon for Simo's arrival. He did not come. Jan tried to call up the fishing boat on the radio without success. We went to the limit of Simo's territory and speculated on what could have happened to the missing dolphin. Turning back towards the harbour, we ran directly into the wind which, despite the sunshine, was very chilly. One of the passengers, looking decidedly green, huddled under the cabin for shelter. Colin got soaked. This is not an auspicious beginning to the film I wanted to make with HTV, I thought, as I tried to distract Colin from his discomfort with the tale of Simo's friendly behaviour the previous evening.

At last we found the dolphin waiting for us at the harbour entrance. David was also there in his little boat. Donning our wetsuits, we were soon in the water with Simo again. Jan anchored and joined us.

I noticed that Simo had spurts of activity, alternating with periods when he did very little. Several times he nuzzled me gently with his beak, after which he would close his eyes and look very peaceful. Then he would swim off to someone else in the water and behave energetically for a few minutes. I also noted that Simo's arrival was the moment at which he was most likely to put his head out of the water for direct eye-to-eye contact. His moods altered from moment to moment. I shall always remember the row of children's faces lined up along the gunwale, peering over the side at Jan and Simo gently playing together.

Simo had changed. He was much more quietly assertive than he had been the year before. Tricia put out her hand and he took it in his mouth. She was not at all distressed. While cavorting in the water we were unaware that those on board were suffering from seasickness. Even in the harbour the boat was rocking, and for us an hour passed very quickly.

Despite the green faces, Colin was pleased with the outcome of his reconnaissance visit to Solva. Immediately we got back to the shore he made up his mind: we were definitely in a 'GO' situation. He was anxious to start filming, and lunch at the Harbour House Hotel was taken amid animated talk of dates and crewing. Before returning to Cardiff, Colin said he would arrange for a contract to be drawn up. I was jubilant, and agreed with Jan to make an early start next day to explore the best locations for filming.

In my diary I recorded Friday, 10 May 1985, as 'the greatest dolphin day ever' – though it didn't start that way . . .

The morning began bright and clear, but by the time we were heading towards the harbour entrance a strong wind was sending clouds scudding across the sky and we needed water-proofs over our wetsuits to keep its icy fingers at bay. We found Simo at the southern extremity of his territory and headed close inshore to the most sheltered position we could find, followed by the dolphin. By this time the sky was completely overcast and the strong eddying wind often whipped up the surface of the sea. Tricia jumped in and did not feel at ease. She said the water was cold and the spray flung in her face uncomfortable. Furthermore, when she laid her arms out on the water, Simo took her hand in his mouth and shook it vigorously. She found this very upsetting. Having won Simo's co-operation I didn't want the other star of my film to quit. Tricia was still nervous in the water because she couldn't swim, and relied totally on the buoyancy of her wetsuit to keep her afloat. I jumped into the sea to reassure her.

Filling my head with music, and visions of couples in elegant period clothes whirling round a glittering ballroom, I took hold of Tricia's hands and swept her into a Viennese waltz. With my legs kicking at full power I propelled us round and round, humming as loudly as I could a Strauss tune as we went. The wind snatched the sounds from my mouth, scattering them over the waves.

Tricia soon forgot about her earlier fright. When she joined in the song, however, Simo quickly descended to examine our flailing fins. Fortunately there were no onlookers, apart from Jan, to witness this crazy scene, which the dolphin enjoyed. He stayed with us, and even poked his head up through our outstretched arms which formed a circle. When the extra-ordinary performance was over, and we snapped back into reality, Tricia felt she had had enough new experiences to last her for a while, and Jan helped her back into the boat. Simo probably thought likewise because he, too, vanished.

I stayed in the water and waited for the dolphin to reappear. When he did so, he was moving slowly, and I discovered that he was much more interested in me if I stayed still in the water – perhaps not altogether surprising in view of my previous behaviour. Although I was still wrapped up in the elation of our interaction a few moments previously, I sensed a distinct change in his mood. I caught hold of Simo's dorsal fin as he glided smoothly underneath me. He towed me for a short distance before I let go.

I then decided to play dead. I had no weightbelt on and just lay back on the surface of the sea, looking straight up at the sky and watching the clouds race by, without any idea what Simo was doing. I could not see him through the restricted vision of my facemask. Nonetheless I was aware of his presence most of the time and could feel him nudging me. Sometimes I turned over, face downwards, with my arms spread-eagled. Simo would not leave me but nudged me continuously.

I then swam over to the rocks and stayed very close inshore with Simo close beside me all the time. Following the line of rocks led me into a cave which went deep into the cliff face. The cave appeared black inside until my eyes adapted to the dark. When I sang out, 'Simo', the word was amplified and bounced around the cave as an impressive echo, momentarily awakening a long-lost, happy childhood memory of shouting 'Hello!' in a tunnel.

Moving forward with my face down was like snorkelling in ink. I could see nothing in the blackness beneath me. As I slowly moved forward I was aware that I was being followed, for I could feel my fins occasionally kicking Simo. It was high water and I continued into the innermost extremity. When I reached the end of the tunnel I stopped and turned round. The opening to the cave appeared as a lighted arch a long way off. There were plopping sounds all around me. Looking up, I could see water dripping from the roof. Near the entrance different coloured minerals in the rocks glistened in the subdued light. I called out, 'Simo, Simo', and listened to the echo. After repeating the dolphin's name, I extended my hands downwards and there beneath me was Simo. I clutched hold of his dorsal fin and he headed towards the entrance of the cave, towing me with him. Several times I thought I would lose my hold, or that he would twist his fin out of my grip, but he didn't. Simo ducked down just below the surface. I hung on as he came up, breathed, and submerged his head again, gliding swiftly and smoothly through the water and pulling me with him. The ride seemed to go on and on. I watched the rockface passing by, and then we were out in the open sea and heading back towards Jan's boat, the *Iolanthe*, which was anchored about eighty metres from the shore. Simo towed me all the way to the ladder of the boat, where I let go of his dorsal fin. Then the tempo picked up even more. We invented a new game, with me pulling myself down the anchor rope, rattling the anchor chain, and then rocketing back to the surface.

I was overjoyed that the dolphin had followed me into the cave and escorted me out again because I felt that this was a sign of his confidence in me.

I had already observed that Simo engaged in bouts of high activity between periods of relative calm, rapidly alternating from one state to the next. How would he like it if his human playmate did the same thing, I wondered. An experiment was called for. Once again, I floated on the surface of the water without moving. Simo nudged and bobbed around me. Then he hung his tail across my chest and let it rest there while I lay in the water gazing up at the sky. Suddenly I displayed a burst of energy and we played a fast game in which I tried to catch Simo and he allowed me to touch him periodically, as if we were playing tag. He often put his tail upright in the water beside me, which may be a sign of possession. Once, when he lowered it slowly, I held it with both hands while he was head down and vertical in the water. He waggled his tail slightly with me holding on to it. I was very amused by the manœuvre. I choked with laughter through my snorkel tube and was sure he sensed the childish pleasure I was getting from his clowning.

Earlier I had taken a camera into the water, and when the film was finished, I had handed it back into the boat, so that in the tunnel and subsequently there were no distractions. Simo and I enjoyed the game, just for the game's sake. After being in the water for an hour I realised that I had had Simo's un-divided attention for the entire time. This was a major break-through and later, I reflected, I had given the dolphin time to familiarise himself thoroughly with me, by lying doggo, before we went into the cave together. Was this one of the clues I was looking for in my search for a better understanding of dolphin psyche?

I was very reluctant to leave the water, and every time I made a gesture of doing so Simo would attempt to dissuade me. He clearly wanted me to stay with him. Physical contact between us increased progressively, to a stage where the dolphin was deliberately rubbing himself up against me vigorously. At times he became excited and we grappled with one another like two rugby players.

After several more games and calm periods I was utterly exhausted. At length I said 'au revoir' to Simo and climbed back on board the *Iolanthe*, knowing that I had just had my best contact with any dolphin to date.

Simo's behaviour vindicated a decision I had made the

previous night while in a state of semi-consciousness. I was reviewing the events of the day just before going to sleep when I came to the conclusion that I should adopt a new approach which required abandoning the scientific method altogether.

The scientific approach demands adherence to a strict and carefully reasoned code of rules. These I understood, and I could appreciate the elegance of some of the experiments designed to find out how dolphins use sonar to explore their world. However, a prerequisite for such studies was the discovery and understanding of sonar. In the area of human-dolphin relationships in which I was interested the fundamental mechanism by which exchanges of feelings and emotions took place had not yet been discovered.

Language is the major pathway through which humans communicate and exchange information. A fact known only too well by politicians is that the use of a single appropriate or inappropriate word can change in seconds the emotional state of a listener from joy to anger, or vice versa. Some scientists have suggested that dolphins also have a language, delphinese. Yet all attempts at analysing the meaning and the content of the train of clicks and whistles that go to make up this hypothetical dolphin language have been fruitless. In contrast we appeared to have made greater headway in unravelling the sounds of the large whales whose lengthy vocalisations have been interpreted as songs through which they pass on their history and exchange stories of their experiences. I felt that a strictly scientific approach was not appropriate if we were to make a breakthrough in comprehending the method by which mental messages were transmitted between humans and dolphins. Instead of employing a carefully reasoned logical method, I felt we should tackle the subject with the impulsive spontaneity of the artist who does not have to justify each stroke before applying brush to canvas.

I had mentioned to Colin Stevens my developing theories on the influence of the Impressionist painters on our present-day understanding of the world. They perceived how light interacted with objects, and expressed it in a manner which had not been seen before. Artists like Monet and van Gogh made many people aware, perhaps for the first time, of the beauty hidden in a landscape, or even in an everyday object, such as a chair. What these painters did may have been regarded as frivolous and of little consequence at the time. Later it became clear that because they opened our minds to new experiences they were, unwittingly perhaps, our teachers.

Most of us think we have an in-built love of nature and of beauty. But we don't. It is as necessary for us to be taught how to value them as it is for us to learn how to cook and sew. Unlike these skills, however, aesthetic appreciation is not usually acquired by the formal processes of teaching and education but creeps slowly into us without our being aware of what is happening.

The Impressionists expanded our awareness, and in doing so broke new ground. The assimilation of their ideas into our culture is still taking place, enabling their visions of reality a hundred years ago to be incorporated in an understanding of the world we see around us today.

As accomplished artists, the Impressionists could have produced paintings that represented their subjects with the sharpness and detail of photographs. Their new art form evolved as a result of them deliberately disregarding convention and the existing rules.

I told Colin that because of my background I was expected to follow a set procedure if I wanted to uncover new and interesting facts about dolphins. The results would eventually be tabulated in encyclopaedias along with weight, length, speed, gestation period and other dolphin data. But I didn't want to do that. If I had an objective at all it was simply to create a greater awareness of the joy dolphins could bring into the lives of humans. The best way I knew of doing this was to make a movie, and in the making of that movie I wanted the freedom to let Simo speak for himself. Who could say how the dolphin would do that until it happened?

I also realised that, in addition to the attitude of an artist, there was another very special quality I needed when setting off on my quest. That was trust in the dolphin – the kind of trust that a child has when jumping fearlessly off a high ledge into the outstretched arms of an adult. Later life will present the grown-up child with a dozen reasons for not jumping. But as a young child, he jumps, and comes to no harm – a new experience is enjoyed that will not be possible in adulthood when the mind is crowded with knowledge, doubts and suspicions.

I needed a framework for my film of course, but I didn't want to work towards preconceived and carefully contrived scenes, as would be done if we were shooting a conventional movie script. By the time I set out with Jan to explore places in which to film the dolphin, I had already decided to sweep away my past. I wanted to approach the film as if I were an artist, and draw what inspiration I could from the subject, namely Simo, itself.

The results of this approach at the end of the first day were better than I would have dared to wish. When I discovered that Simo was keeping me company in the cave, I felt as though I had made a brief excursion into the dark recesses of his mind. By acting on impulse and intuition I had come closer than ever before to understanding the aquatic alien to which many people are emotionally, yet inexplicably, attracted. Seeing Tricia on the stern as she peered into the grey water, watching the dolphin slide effortlessly alongside us like a grey shadow, I knew she was an ideal person through whom to explore the human-dolphin relationship on film.

When, after lunch, the time came to leave the Harbour House Hotel, Tricia emerged looking as if she had just stepped from the pages of *Vogue* magazine, transformed from a sea urchin playing with dolphins to a high-powered agent whose next task was to negotiate a contract for me with the hard-headed businessmen of HTV.

By the time we arrived at HTV several people there had seen on the front page of the *Western Mail* a photograph of Simo with Tricia and were interested to meet her. One of them, the producer John Mead, listened intently to Tricia's account of her love of dolphins and immediately asked her to take part in the *Elinor Show*. Appearing in a chat show was something she had not expected. The prospect terrified her, but reluctantly she agreed and gave no hint of the turmoil and devastating insecurity with which she was filled.

The Chopper Turns Out

I was excited by the prospect of working with Colin Stevens on a film about Simo because his background was not in fact-filled documentaries but with international stars like Tom Jones and Shirley Bassey. Now he was going to work with a dolphin whose presence on the set could never be guaranteed and whose services could not be bought at any price. It would be a challenge for Colin as well as for me.

Our original plan was to film Simo and his developing relationship with Tricia and the inhabitants of Solva over the period of a year. The story would be told against the seasonal changes that took place in a picturesque Welsh fishing village. In the end it turned out to be a romantic story, but as so often happens with the making of documentary films it did not break down into the neat four seasonal components I originally proposed. This was firstly because the summer of 1985 barely existed, and secondly because, with the onset of autumn, Simo vanished. None the less we had shot enough material by then to edit the footage into an engaging film. There were some moments of very high drama, but these occurred when things went wrong in rough weather and did not appear in the final film. We also had many notable swims with Simo, one of which was very special for Tricia.

Unless they are directly involved with film production, very few people have much idea of the amount of gear that is assembled and preparation that takes place before filming begins – especially under water. Perhaps even more of an eye-opener is the infinite trouble taken to get a new or extra dramatic shot. Tricia was amazed to see Mick Reynolds arrive in Solva with his HTV Volvo packed from floor to roof with camera equipment. What came as more of a shock to her were the lengths to which I expected her to go in gaining footage for the film.

In the morning, as we returned from West Wales Divers near Broadhaven with more diving equipment, the sky was intensely blue and a strong cold wind, coming straight off the sea, fetched up white horses. Rank upon rank of them charged with inexhaustible energy on to the long yellow strand where the wind whipped off their heads and flung them as spume at grassy hillocks that bordered a long stretch of beach. Pebbles that had been bulldozed by the sea into huge mounds were scattered across the roadway at Newgale. The sea had a soft, slightly yellow hue which I knew indicated that underwater visibility was poor. I decided to concentrate on getting some dolphin point of view shots (or P.O.V.'s) using the camera in its underwater housing at sea level in the more sheltered waters of the harbour.

The Arriflex BL camera, heavy and bulky inside its water-proof housing, was mounted on one of the circular cork lifebelts from the *Iolanthe*. With this set up I could get a sequence I particularly wanted – a shot from water level of Tricia jumping into the sea.

Now leaping into the water was something she had never done before, and she still regarded just floating in the sea with considerable trepidation unless there was a dolphin near by to divert her attention. She was starting nevertheless to get the hang of using fins for propulsion as well as for keeping herself upright in the water. In that position she could take the rapid gasps of air necessary to sustain life with a racing heartbeat. All this considered, I judged her to be advanced enough to jump into the sea from the bow of the *Iolanthe*, no more than two metres above water.

Tricia saw the situation differently. Firstly, the sea looked a long way down when she stood on the deck. To her, jumping off the *Iolanthe* was little different to flinging herself from the top of the Empire State Building. Secondly, even when young she had never had the slightest inclination, or the physique, for adventure sports, so that now as a grandmother she felt safely past the stage at which anyone might reasonably expect her to engage in such dangerous and demanding activities. Thirdly, she knew that she would go under as soon as she hit the water. I had to use all my persuasive power to assure her she would rise to the surface again afterwards. I knew I couldn't very well ask her to re-enact that first leap at a later stage, so I omitted to tell her that I wanted to capture the genuine look of shock and surprise I knew she would show when she surfaced.

Simo co-operated with my plan and came into the harbour out of the gale. At noon we loaded the *Iolanthe* with our experimental camera float and joined the dolphin. When I had got everything set up in the water, I asked Tricia to go up on to the bow and jump when I gave her the word, 'Action!' Until that moment she hadn't thought I was serious about asking her to leap into the sea. Suddenly, she realised I meant it.

She stood on deck looking down at me bobbing in the sea a thousand feet below, and froze.

I looked up at her and pressed the button. 'Okay,' I shouted up. 'Camera's running. Action!'

Nothing happened. She stood there petrified.

'ACTION!' I shouted again. Still nothing.

'For Christ's sake, Tricia,' I screamed at her. 'Get your arse into gear and jump!'

She plummeted beside me, then emerged, eyes popping, more than surprised to find herself still alive.

Simo came over to see what all the shouting was about and Tricia told him what the nasty cameraman had persuaded her to do. She little knew that was just a warm-up for what was to come.

After lunch, we were back in the entrance to the harbour which was guarded by a sinister sentinel called Black Rock. The way in which the sea reacts to this rock depends upon the strength and direction of the wind, as well as the state of the tide. On the afternoon of 12 June 1985 the angry sea was bombarding the rock as if attempting to drive it back into the harbour. The fight had been going on for centuries, but time had shown that such assaults were to no avail. The rock always won, shredding its adversary into white foam and hurling it back on itself, creating a heaving, disarranged mass of seething swirling water. The resulting turmoil was treacherous for vessels and small boats alike. It was also spectacular to watch – especially from the south cliff, known as the Gribin, which formed one side of the natural entrance to Solva harbour. The viewing points on the headland were well peppered with sightseers, including many kept from their boats by the wild weather.

One of the spectators was Anne Marks, who had alerted me to the presence of the dolphin in Solva and so had more than a passing interest in what we were doing as we anchored the *Iolanthe* at the limit of protected water in the harbour entrance.

When shooting the film *A Closer Encounter*, I had been lured by the dolphin Jean Louis into the boiling water off Dolphin Rock in Brittany. That experience had taught me that it was possible to swim safely very close to rocks so long as I avoided being dashed on to them – which was what had happened to an unfortunate man fishing from the base of the cliffs while I was there. He had lost his life, and his body was hauled out of the water by helicopter close to where we were filming.

In Solva the conditions were similar to those in Brittany on that fateful day, but Jan Sendall was an experienced sailor who knew just how close to Black Rock it was safe to take his boat. Also aboard the *Iolanthe* was Mick Reynolds, who had been assigned to us by HTV because he had a reputation as an adventurous cameraman. A good sailor, though not a diver, Mick enjoyed boating under wild conditions but had never been in a position to test my theory about getting close to the rocks. He was about to do just that.

Tricia was the only other person aboard the *Iolanthe*. For her, a rowing boat ride on the Serpentine in Hyde Park would have been something of an adventure. She knew nothing of boats, tides, or the ways of the sea. Theoretically, she should have been the least willing of us to venture out that afternoon, but she wasn't. She had absolute faith in Jan. During her previous voyage in very rough water Tricia had shown that once on board the *Iolanthe* she had no fear of the sea whatever.

We were about to start shooting. I wanted to show the dolphin in its natural environment in all types of weather, and the gale provided just what was needed for rough sea sequences. Having anchored the *Iolanthe*, Jan was to row Tricia out to Black Rock in the small fibreglass dinghy he used as a tender while I filmed a view of her in the white water with Black Rock in the background. This dolphin's-eye-view would be confirmed by splicing it to a shot of Simo swimming up to Tricia on the surface in the same location.

Wild weather excited Tricia. Still feeling immortal having survived her leap into the sea off the bow of the *Iolanthe*, she was positively enthusiastic about the proposal. When the camera was loaded and handed to me in the water, she climbed down into the tender and sat on the stern seat. Jan took his place amidships and, facing Tricia, began to row away from the *Iolanthe*. I was in the water pushing the camera on its float ahead of me.

After seeing everyone off the *Iolanthe*, Mick, with the nonchalance only a cameraman who has seen it all and done it all can muster, settled down on the floor of the boat, in the sun and out of the wind, to read a book. Those watching from the shore were more than a little surprised to see the tiny dinghy bobbing on the water, moving closer and closer to Black Rock. It must have been a very colourful sight from that vantage point: Tricia, dressed in a bright red wetsuit, beaming with excitement, her black hair flying in the wind, contrasting with Jan's rugged, stern features and greying beard. He wore a navy-blue fisherman's pullover with IOLANTHE emblazoned in capital letters across his chest, looking every inch a salty sea-dog.

Facing the back of the boat, Jan couldn't see where he was going unless he looked over his shoulder. He took directions from me, and I urged him closer and closer to the rocks that periodically rose like glistening black teeth from the engulfing foam.

I had a wide-angle lens on the camera, which makes distant objects look very small. I knew, therefore, that to achieve the effect I wanted I would have to get Tricia very near to the rocks indeed. Those watching from shore were horrified when they saw what we were doing. I was oblivious to their concern and urged Jan to go even closer.

It was exhilarating to work with someone as skilled as Jan. He had complete control of his boat but had to pull very hard on the oars to keep the bow into the wind. He rose and fell like a cork with the oncoming waves. From my viewpoint at water level, and a short distance away, there were times when he reared above me. At others I looked down on him in the trough while I rose on the crest.

Just when we reached the limit which I considered to be safe for all of us, disaster struck. One of Jan's oars snapped in two. He immediately lost control. The tiny boat spun sideways to the wind, and at that moment the extra big wave that arrives periodically in all rough conditions came surging past Black Rock. The dinghy rose up on to its hissing crest. The snarling wind lifted the little boat off the top of the waves and flipped it over, pitching its occupants into the foam.

With nothing to weigh the frail craft down, the wind mercilessly took hold of it and carried it like a used paper bag across the narrow channel to another outcrop of rocks, where it was smashed to pieces in seconds. Jan grabbed the oar and other bits of floating wreckage for buoyancy. Tricia suddenly found herself in a swirling mass of white foam alongside fangs of rock over which the sea cascaded with a roar.

All this was witnessed by the crowd which had gathered on the headland. Terrified, they watched the dinghy capsize, and expected Jan and Tricia to perish with it.

Anne Marks knew that Tricia couldn't swim and screamed across to Mick, now enjoying a bottle of wine and smoked salmon sandwiches in the *Iolanthe*. The harbour master, known to everyone, ourselves included, as Sharkey, was also alerted. He immediately telephoned the nearby RAF Brawdy, where a full-scale helicopter rescue was launched.

I was unaware of all this, as was Tricia, whose only concern was for her own survival. Not unnaturally, she expected me to abandon the camera and rush to her rescue at once. Yet I knew that the wave that had pitched her into the sea had also carried her past the danger point. Provided she stayed afloat the wind, the waves and the incoming tide would eventually bring her into the safety of the harbour. I pressed the shutter button and, pushing the camera in Tricia's general direction on its float, started filming.

Meanwhile the alarm had been well and truly raised. Mick started the *Iolanthe*'s engine, rushed to the bow and hauled in the anchor.

One of the visiting boats moored in the harbour had a small inflatable tied to its stern. The owner unhitched it and set off towards Black Rock to offer assistance. By this time the three of us in the water were grouped together and drifting into harbour.

The boatman peered at me over the side of his inflatable with a look of astonishment and said, 'You're Horace Dobbs, aren't you? Do you know that at this very moment my wife is down in the cabin of our boat reading your book, "Follow a Wild Dolphin"?'

Our conversation terminated as Mick hove to with the *Iolanthe*. No sooner were we on board than the next of our would-be saviours arrived. The air reverberated with the unmistakable whirling of rotor blades. The sea around us was flattened like a putting green on a bunker-strewn golf course by the downdraft from the helicopter overhead. The winchman called down to us through his loudhailer and we signalled back that we were all safe. Tricia, who took the whole episode with uncharacteristic equanimity, let it be known afterwards she was disappointed that we were rescued so promptly. She said she had always wanted to be winched up into a helicopter.

· 8 ·

The Wreck

One result of our ordeal at Black Rock was that Tricia's confidence in the sea took a quantum leap forward. It proved to her beyond all doubt that when she was wearing her thick Beaver wetsuit she couldn't sink. Bobbing around on the surface like a cork, Tricia discovered that if she just lay on her back and thrashed her fins she moved through the water. With her face clear of the water all the time her breathing was unrestricted. Soon she was finning backwards at speed. The next stage was learning to use the mask and snorkel. This skill took a little longer to acquire, but she mastered it in a couple of days. Floating in a prone position, she could see down into the water through the mask while at the same time breathing through the snorkel tube. A gentle crawl stroke with her fins, and she was moving forwards. The incentive for doing this certainly did not spring from any desire to achieve sporting prowess, or even vanity because we were making a film. It arose from her desperate need to be able to swim with Simo in the sea. Simo, for his part, enjoyed the company of the female human who was making so much effort to share her time with him. As Tricia's snorkelling ability progressed so the bond between her and the dolphin grew rapidly.

Surfacing alongside our boat, Simo would recognise Tricia not just from her bright red wetsuit, but also from her demeanour, for she always hung over the side and talked to him. She often referred to Simo as her 'baby' and would excitedly call to him, 'Hello Baby', as soon as he swam up to the *Iolanthe*. If Tricia didn't get into the water immediately, and we fiddled with cameras or other equipment on board, the dolphin would circle the boat looking for other things to amuse himself until Tricia joined him.

After the loss of his dinghy Jan acquired a new tender which he towed behind the *Iolanthe*. One day I noticed Simo playing around this boat, where he appeared to be interested in a metal shackle dangling from the rope that attached the dinghy to a sternpost on the *Iolanthe*. As the boats moved the shackle bobbed up and down. Simo rose out of the water to watch it, his head swaying from side to side as he did so. Then he knocked the shackle repeatedly with his beak – rather like a kitten patting a piece of paper tied to the end of a length of string.

The new toy was immediately abandoned when Tricia jumped into the sea – which she now did without a moment's hesitation, from the highest part of the bow of the *Iolanthe*. Once in the water her antics with Simo stretched to the limits of her snorkelling ability. When she discovered how to use her fins to pirouette, she promptly performed a short aquatic ballet for Simo's benefit to show him her new-found skill. She said she felt like a water-borne ballerina.

She told me later that the moment she first learnt how to twirl around in the water was very important to her, for it was then that she really mastered the use of fins and discovered how to manœuvre herself wherever she wanted. Once she found she was in full control she finally lost the last traces of a terror of the open water that she had carried with her since childhood. Before meeting the dolphin she had not even ventured into a shallow swimming pool.

We decided to film around the two wrecked tugs which had been driven on to the rocks during a storm. Future storms would tear the wrecks to pieces and the waves, attacking them like vultures, would peck at the iron carrion until only the ribs and the iron engine blocks were left. In time even they would go, inexorably digested into the sea by erosion and corrosion.

The dispersal process was already well under way for one of the vessels had broken in two.

The other, however, was still intact. It had been pushed by the waves and the wind head-on to the shore, where it was firmly lodged at the base of a cliff. The forward part of the stricken vessel remained above water at all states of the tide, while the keel at the stern lay always under water. When the tide rose, water flooded into the ship, pouring through doorways and other openings which were themselves eventually engulfed by the rising water.

I chose the giant metallic corpse at the foot of magnificent towering cliffs as a location partly because it was visually spectacular, but also as evidence of the nature of the sea, at times alluringly beautiful and peaceful, at others savage and brutal. These were the extremes of the dolphin's world that I wanted to capture in our film.

One of the major influences on the moods of the sea is the moon, for it is the magnetic pull of the moon that creates and regulates the tides. The moon therefore directly influenced our activities in Solva. With the tide cycle of 12 hours and 25 minutes, the harbour would empty and fill twice a day, high water occurring about 50 minutes later each day. That meant adjusting our timetable from day to day to coincide with times when Jan could bring the *Iolanthe* alongside the jetty to load and unload our gear. When the tide was out, the inlet dried except for the stream which fed into it. Any boats left at their moorings in the inner harbour were grounded as the tide receded and then keeled over on the sand at low water.

It was one o'clock when Jan pulled alongside the jetty and we transferred the underwater camera from the Volvo. Simo was waiting for us outside the harbour and encouraged by Tricia's joyful welcome tucked in behind us to see where we were going. We turned north-west out of the harbour entrance, and it seemed no time at all before we rounded a headland and the wreck came into view.

As soon as we were in position and Jan threw the anchor overboard Simo dived straight down to inspect it. All the friendly dolphins I have swum with have been fascinated by anchors, and Simo was no exception. We had discovered when we were working with the dolphin Jean Louis in France that rattled anchor chains produce high frequency sounds which are outside the range of human hearing but which would be clearly audible to dolphins. I wondered if it was partly the unusual sound of the anchor chain that attracted dolphins. On the other hand, the crunching sound produced as the anchor fluke cuts a furrow in the sand before it is embedded would also be heard by the dolphin, who doubtless would be curious to see what was ploughed up. Whatever the explanation, Simo's attention was riveted on the anchor when we were mooring. This meant that he was unlikely to swim away to an alternative source of interest, for a short time at least.

Having established that we were properly anchored, Simo popped his head out of the water and looked at Tricia who, as usual, was hanging over the side to see what he was doing. While I got into full diving regalia, Mick loaded the camera into its housing and Jan brought his new dinghy alongside.

'Come on, Tricia, jump in.'

With the dolphin trailing him Jan rowed to the hulk to give Tricia a close-up view and keep the dolphin amused. After returning to the *Iolanthe*, he lifted the aqualung cylinder, complete with its regulator, on to my back and checked that it was comfortable. I sat on the gunwale. He then made sure that Simo was not underneath me before I rolled backwards, to drop cylinder-first and with a great splash, into the sea.

Hitting the sea felt like being squirted from a giant soda siphon. I knew what to expect – a few seconds of disorientation, during which I was enveloped in a cascade of air bubbles, before I could manœuvre my body into an upright position in the water. I exhaled and allowed myself to sink, pulled down by gravity, gently and slowly into the depths. Automatically I ran through the check list, making sure my mask was sealed properly before finning up to the surface to give Jan the okay sign – a thumb and forefinger held together to form a circle. I held up my hand and Jan encircled my wrist with the lanyard attached to my underwater light meter. Next came the bulky camera housing which he lowered to me on a rope. Above water it weighed nearly 100 lbs, but in the water it was virtually weightless. It did present a large additional surface area, however, that created extra resistance when it came to swimming through the water. I headed off towards the bow, where the anchor rope was hanging in a graceful curve, and disappeared into a green haze.

Simo could not have been more co-operative as Jan started the engine, pulled in the anchor, and then went through the entire anchoring routine again. The dolphin oversaw the operation like a zealous chief petty officer aboard a tightly run ship. He swam up and down the chain, with the tip of his pointed beak almost touching it, examining every link. As the anchor trailed across the sea-bed, setting up a trail of sand clouds, he followed the action keenly, and when the flukes spiked into the sand and Jan gave an extra heave to make sure it would hold, the dolphin nodded his head vigorously, signifying his approval.

My joy at shooting just the sequence I wanted was short-lived. When Mick opened the camera housing he told me the battery was dead. I had exposed only 50 feet and not 300 feet as I had thought. The camera was rehoused and connected to a fully recharged battery for the next sequence. This time we lowered it to Jan in the rowing boat. Then Tricia and I climbed down and Jan rowed right up to the hulk with the dolphin following behind us.

Tugs are steel-clad workhorses, compact and very robust, whose insides are filled with mighty engines that provide the power to push and pull much larger vessels. There are no embellishments on a tug, everything is functional. With the sea sweeping over its stern winches, the wrecked tug we were approaching had lost its former aggressiveness and barnacles encrusting the hull muted the severity of its appearance. Fronds of seaweed and bits of discarded fishing net covered with moss-like green algae and attached to the stern rail wafted back and forth with each successive wave.

So as not to upset the dinghy I rolled very gently backwards over the transom into the sea. I was joined by Tricia a few moments later, and then Jan lifted the camera overboard. I took it and sank gently down. Looking up, I watched Tricia's progress as she finned along the edge of the ship, looking down at the catwalk between the rail and superstructure where tough merchant seamen once strode.

Acting as Tricia's guide, Simo moved along the narrow alley way, his body as bright and smooth as polished steel. Sunlight refracted by the waves above, dappled the dolphin and the ship with dancing patterns of amber light.

The door to the engine room was missing and the opening was almost completely submerged. It was a major passageway for water and each passing wave caused the sea to surge into, and then out of the rectangular hole. I swam over to it and looked in. The hollow vessel acted as a shock absorber, transforming the lumpy movements of the waves outside to a gentle heaving motion inside.

At first it appeared to be totally black within the hull except for the pencils of light that penetrated the chamber through holes in the deck, shining through the water like laser beams. As my eyes adapted to the darkness the massive metal block of the engine and steel girders materialised as chocolate-brown solid images. I allowed a wave to push me into the wreck and turned to face the opening. There, perfectly framed in the doorway was the face of Simo, watching me anxiously – or was it curiously? I wedged myself in position so that I would not be swept back and forth by the surging water, framed the picture in the viewfinder and pressed the shutter button. Simo nodded his head up and down, as if in approval, and stayed exactly where he was with no apparent effort, despite the back and forth flow of the water that took all my strength to resist. When he moved off, a new face appeared at the opening. It was Tricia's. She managed to stay in position by holding on to the sides of the framed opening with her gloved hands. I filmed her too, before emerging from the gloom of the wreck to return to the blue, sun-filled, open sea.

·9·

Falling for a Dolphin

The memory of Simo perfectly framed and peering in at me when I was inside the wrecked tug is one of those magic images that has stayed with me like a treasured snapshot in a photograph album. For Tricia, however, it was an incident some weeks later that was to become enshrined in her memory as one of the most highly prized moments in her life. It took place on a day which Mick Reynolds, our cameraman, wished had never happened, and would dearly like to forget. That day was 8 July 1985.

'Simo is definitely off colour, Horace,' Jan said to me when we drove on to the jetty at noon.

We had returned to Solva to find everyone concerned about Simo. During the past week, we were told, the dolphin had been listless, would allow no physical contact, and just swam slowly in a circle around those who got into the sea with him.

We loaded the *Iolanthe* once again with our cameras and diving gear, not knowing what to expect. A slightly apprehensive atmosphere prevailed as Jan, with Tricia, myself and Mick the cameraman on board, steered the *Iolanthe* away from the jetty.

Jan's eagle eye spotted Simo playing with a pot marker buoy shortly after we left the harbour entrance. Tricia let out a shriek of delight when she saw the dolphin. She hung over the side and dipped her hand in the water. Simo immediately came to it and nudged it with his beak. As she stroked him the dolphin raised his head further out of the water. Tricia ran her fingers up and down his throat murmuring softly, 'Oh baby, oh baby I love you.' She was in heaven again, enjoying the sensual satin-soft feel of Simo's pale skin beneath her slender sensitive fingers. For Tricia, touch was very important – when enjoying the beauty of a flower she invariably stroked it with her fingers as well as smelling it and admiring its colour and shape. Jan put the engine into neutral for Tricia's reunion with Simo. When they had finished greeting one another, he engaged gear again and opened the throttle. We could feel the engine's powerful throb through the deck. As we continued our journey round the coast towards the wrecked tug the dolphin took up his usual station astern. Simo moved effortlessly and silently through the water, giving us occasional glimpses of his white underbelly when he arched away from us to weave his own pattern of motion in the sea.

During the interval since our last visit the camera housing, which was on hire, had been returned to London for some modifications. I was pleased with the new viewfinder that had been added, and left Mick to encase his very expensive Arriflex camera, loaded with a new magazine of film and a fully recharged battery, in its bright orange housing while I sorted out my diving equipment. Carefully he checked that all was working well before slating it – that is, holding a clapper board containing details of the location and so on in front of the camera and running off a few frames so that the editor could later identify when and where that section of film was shot.

When we were moored off the tug, in the same location as previously, I jumped into the sea to take the sequences of Simo with the anchor which I had failed to shoot on our previous visit. The dolphin was just as co-operative as before. I watched him through the new viewfinder, measured the light intensity, and turned the camera round to adjust the lens aperture. To my horror, I saw water through the lens porthole inside the camera housing. I rushed to the surface. Jan had the camera back in the boat within seconds. Before I could get back into the boat Mick had the housing open and was draining the sea water out of his precious camera. While I took off my diving gear and dried myself he stripped down the camera and sprayed it with an oil aerosol. But complex live electronic circuitry and sea water are totally incompatible. The camera was useless and would probably cost several thousand pounds to restore to full working order.

The cause of the flooding was obvious the moment Mick opened the housing. There was no tension on the spring clips holding the two components of the waterproof case together. They had been slackened when the housing was away. Mick had not noticed this when he snapped them into position. It was a very expensive lesson, one which neither of us would forget. The atmosphere on board the *Iolanthe* was as heavy as lead. Not only had we lost a camera, we had lost a filming opportunity when conditions were as perfect as they were ever likely to be. And to crown it all, despite the pessimistic forecast, Simo's behaviour indicated that, if he *had* been ill, he had since made a full recovery. Furthermore, he was anxiously waiting for someone to get in the water to play with him.

After the first muted explosion of anguish we all realised that no amount of brooding over the catastrophe would put it right. Mick wanted to be left alone to salvage what pieces of his camera he could. The rest of us wanted to get away from the *Iolanthe*. So Jan rowed over to the tug to explore the part of the stricken vessel that was above water level, while Tricia and I jumped into the sea to explore the gulleys and channels that were forming around the rocks as the tide fell.

It was a new experience for Tricia. She was warm and comfortable floating on the surface and looking down at the sea-bed beneath her. For her, it was like a low-level helicopter ride over the undersea channels formed by the rocks that reared out of the water around us. Sand eels, flashing like strips of tinsel in the sun, wriggled their way ahead of us. Small shoals of pouting fled when our black silhouettes drifted across their sky. They probably mistook us for seals. Tricia was as bemused and excited as a child.

I climbed out on to a rock covered with slippery seaweed and tried to pull Tricia up after me, but she slipped and fell back into the sea, laughing. Tricia wanted to dance for joy. Holding

1 Simo and I enjoy an energetic game together
near Solva in Wales

2-3 Tails and heads: this is not a mermaid touching her own tail, but Tricia in a buoyant wetsuit, making her first contact with Simo near Solva

4-5 Bill Bowell, a chronic depressive who had not worked for many years, was a changed man from the moment he first touched a dolphin. As a result, I set up Operation Sunflower to find out how dolphins seemed able to blow away the blues.

6 David Canby-Lewis was one of the first people to
befriend Simo the dolphin who loved being gently stroked
with an oar or a boat hook

hands we spun round in the water, singing 'Ring a ring of roses,' as we twirled. Simo joined in the dance and then jumped over us in a state of unbridled ecstasy.

Jan too was infected with a desire to return to childhood. From afar we could hear him banging with his hammer inside the wreck. Then he emerged like a jack-in-the-box out of the top of the funnel. He shouted over to us and triumphantly brandished his hammer in the air. He was a boy again. Who knew what treasure he might find there, exploring the wreck?

I took Tricia's hand and led her along gulleys and over the forest of kelp, pointing out crabs, lobsters, starfish, anemones and some of the other inhabitants of the undersea world. I even spotted a plaice, covered with sand with only its eyes protruding. Simo remained with us wherever we went, and when it looked as if we were becoming too preoccupied with the scenery, he decided it was time we gave him some special attention. He swam up from underneath us, so that his dorsal fin slipped into our interlocked hands. For the next few minutes we did not have to swim – Simo towed us. I let go when I spotted another flat-fish. I turned to point it out to Tricia, but she had her mind on other things. She wanted to stroke Simo, and from his response there was no doubt that he wanted her to do so. As I watched I could hear incomprehensible words bubbling out of her snorkel tube. I swam away and continued to browse, enjoying the simple pleasure of just looking, with no camera or responsibilities to intrude on my reverie. Tricia, for her part, abandoned herself to Simo, physically and emotionally. She cupped her hands around his dorsal fin and he ferried her away. No fairytale knight on a white charger ever carried a more willing maiden away more purposefully. But I tell you this is no fairytale, for I watched the dolphin take his prize away, right out of the bay.

At a later date I filmed one of Simo's attempts to abduct Tricia, for after that he did it frequently. Whereas he towed me from the cave towards the boat, he always took Tricia away from the *Iolanthe*. There were times when he even tried to prevent her from returning to the boat.

Here is how Tricia described her experience when I asked her to write down what happened while it was still fresh in her mind:

Simo surfaced a few yards away and swam towards me, coming up on the righthand side of my body. I put my cupped hands around his dorsal fin as he slowly passed. I have no explanation as to why I did so. It was purely spontaneous. He did not attempt to roll over and dislodge my hands. I wasn't holding on tightly, my hands were just resting on his dorsal fin.

The dolphin moved quite slowly at first, then gradually built up speed until we were flying through the water like Concorde. It was electrifying. I had no thoughts of letting go, no fear, only love. I felt like a Princess being taken away to another land by her Prince, her knight in shining armour. My Prince was taking me into his world beyond the realms of all fantasy. There was no sound. No one else in the entire world, only us two. We were together as one. It seemed as if we would go on forever without stopping. Travelling the seas and depths of the ocean, I was him and he was me. Complete harmony and love.

No words could possibly describe the wonderful sensation and happiness I felt as Simo towed me a long way and then gently rolled over, leaving me floating on the surface of the water. Floating in every sense of the word. Simo did not go away. He stayed very close, swimming around me. He then lay beside me, content as I stroked him with my finger tips not wishing to break the spell. The towering cliffs watched us in silence. No sounds invaded the magic bubble we were in. I did not speak, we communicated with our hearts. I was totally and completely in love, and it was surging throughout every part of my body. Every nerve was on fire. Simo and I were two lovers in the depths of the sea. This beautiful dolphin loved me for what was in my heart. It didn't matter whether I was old, young, fat or thin. I didn't have to impress him with a string of degrees. I was loved and accepted for myself, for the person I was. Simo was far superior to me in every way in the water. I did not have to compete, all the stresses of human values and life no longer existed.

The whole episode seemed to happen in slow motion. I resumed my upright position, treading water with my fins. He put his beak against my chest and gently pushed me back through the water. Then he nudged me with his beak as if to say, 'You follow me.' Simo could move with a speed, energy and power I could only dream of. And yet he was playing with me. I could do nothing to entertain him, he entertained me. I lifted my head and could see the boat in the distance and a small red blob that seemed to be moving in my direction. It was obviously Horace. I just lay back on the surface of the water with the sun on my face, dreaming, full of wonderment, looking up at the soft blue sky above me and enjoying the love that was swelling in my heart.

I heard Horace shout, 'Tricia'. I looked up into his face that had an expression of total amazement. He said, 'I turned around and you were flying through the water at such a speed. What a fantastic tow. Simo took you for miles.' We chatted as Horace stroked Simo gently down his body. It occurred to me that Simo's tail had been thrashing up and down a couple of inches away from my stomach, and yet it did not hit me. Dolphins can move with incredible precision.

Horace then suggested we make our way back to the boat, which was a long way off. I did not think I could make it. But Horace assured me I could, and said, 'We can take it in stages, resting when you're tired.' It was such a beautiful day and there was no immediate hurry. As I lay on the surface looking into the depths, the softness of the water on my face felt wonderful. My mask enabled me to see the sandy bottom that cut its way along the sea-bed. It looked like a motorway, but instead of cars hurtling along, shoals of tiny fish streamed along the gulley. It was a spectacular sight enhanced by the vivid colours of the rocks and of the seaweeds that looked like ballet dancers dressed in olive-green and rich ruby-red costumes. The setting for their underwater performance was an Aladdin's cave composed of diversely coloured rocks and stones being the jewels. I felt so beautiful and totally part of the beauty set before me. How I wished I could hold my breath and dive down into Simo's world. It was so wonderful. It was more than a dream come true.

Simo would swim underneath us, then disappear and surface behind us. He would dive a few feet down and come up with his belly uppermost and rub it against Horace, or myself, to impede our progress. We would stop, stroke him, then try and continue on. Eventually we reached the boat. Simo swam down and nudged the anchor with his beak. Horace duck-dived into the depths of the clear water and pulled on the anchor rope, much to Simo's delight. The dolphin had obviously recovered his energy after towing me, and was now ready for a game with Horace. I was lying on the surface of the water watching them play like two children. Horace would occasionally surface for a gulp of air before diving down again to join Simo. Now and then I could hear a puff as Simo surfaced to do the same thing. But he did not need to surface as frequently as Horace.

Simo would swim right up and put his beak on the glass of Horace's facemask. I'm sure he was reading Horace's mind, to see what his human friend would do next. They played underwater tag with Simo in hot pursuit when Horace dived. At the end of the game they both surfaced. Simo stretched two-thirds of his body right out of the water, and Horace cuddled him. How happy they were. But that is one of the wonderful things about dolphins – they make everybody happy.

Unfortunately, it was time to go.

· 10 ·

Lessons in Diving and Life

The strength of the bond between Tricia and Simo was obvious to all who sailed aboard the *Iolanthe*. One of those who joined us on a dolphin-watching trip was Kieran Mulvaney, who was well known for his strictly analytical but sensitive approach to the cetaceans. His observations on how close Tricia and Simo had become were recorded in Wade Doak's beautifully illustrated book, *Encounters with Whales and Dolphins*.

There were a lot of people down to see the dolphin and they all got in at once. This meant there were really far too many in the water for one dolphin – about eight – especially as Simo seems happiest when he has just one person to play with. What made things worse this time was the presence of Tricia Kirkman. Simo adores this incredibly warm, sensitive woman, who can't swim the width of a pool, but clad in a wetsuit, gambols with Simo like a good swimmer.

Well, from the beginning it was clear Simo wanted her to himself. When all the swimmers formed a circle, Simo pushed Tricia away from the rest. He took her on about four tows within less than a quarter hour. Whenever anybody else tried to intervene he let them know they were not wanted. He bit two people, drawing blood, and he buffeted another around the head with his tail. Eventually everyone else left the water and he played with Tricia alone.

Tricia openly admitted that she loved Simo. If such an emotional bond can extend from a human to a dolphin then, in view of what we know about dolphins, I do not think it unreasonable to suggest that such a relationship could work both ways, and that Simo loved Tricia.

The affinity between them became even more poignant and obvious to me when it was time for Tricia to learn to use the aqualung. Simo's devotion to Tricia certainly made filming the episode much easier for me than it might otherwise have been. A very understanding instructor from West Wales Divers, Mike Durnford, was recruited to take her down into Simo's world for the first time. He sat Tricia on the side of an inflatable boat and carefully explained the function of the various pieces of equipment before kitting her up. First, an adjustable buoyancy life jacket was pulled over her head and strapped round her waist and between her legs. After that came the regulator which she had to keep in her mouth and bite with her teeth. This provided her air supply from a heavy metal cylinder that was tightly fastened to her body to prevent it swinging about in the water. Finally he encircled her with a belt strung with 20 lbs of lead weights. This was pulled tightly around her waist and fastened with a quick-release buckle.

Many people find wearing a thick wetsuit claustrophobic because it is so restricting. When encumbered by a full set of aqualung diving equipment, even the most experienced of divers feels like a trussed chicken. For somebody of Tricia's slim build the combined weight and restriction of all the gear made just standing up difficult for her.

The first time anyone gets fully kitted up to go aqualung diving they cannot help wondering just how they are ever going to be able to get back to the surface again once they have committed themselves to the deep. The surprise comes when they are in the water, for in the sea they become weightless, and any movement of the hands or fins will send them up, down, or even sideways.

Quite naturally Tricia was more than a little nervous when she first lowered herself over the side of the inflatable into the sea. She was, in fact, terrified. Like all novices her respiration rate was fast. Her instructor took her hands to reassure her.

Facing one another the two of them sank slowly towards the canopy of bright green *Laminaria* seaweed that covered the rocks. She could hear the air emerging from her regulator and gurgling up past her face. As she looked into her instructor's facemask Tricia realised that she was several feet beneath the surface – and still breathing. Indeed, it was as easy to inhale from the regulator under water as it was on the surface. She had made what a few months before would have seemed an utterly impossible transformation. She, Tricia, was actually under the sea, breathing.

Mike Durnford let go of one of her hands and Tricia looked around in wide-eyed wonderment. The sun was shining, the new world she had entered was aglow with blue light. She was drifting over a gently swaying forest of seaweed, the large fronds of the *Laminaria* looking like waving palm trees. Gliding through this sun-filled enchanted forest came Simo. He passed slowly and transfixed her with his eye. Tricia looked back at him and tried to transmit the thought to Simo that she had come down to join him in his world beneath the waves.

If ever I saw a dolphin emit a feeling of tenderness and love then I witnessed it that day as I filmed Tricia's first aqualung dive. Slowly Simo circled her, watching her every move. He seemed to appoint himself as Tricia's guardian, and would see to it that she came to no harm. He would show her the secrets of the realm of the Water Babies, one of the places she had often drifted into in her imagination.

Viewers of the finished film were astonished to see Tricia, who could barely swim, scuba diving with a powerful dolphin. To Tricia herself, it was miraculous.

She had arrived in the world two months early, one of twin girls weighing less than three pounds. They were taken from their mother, bathed in olive oil, carefully wrapped in cotton-wool and put in a drawer, where they were fed with milk from a glass dropper. Both girls survived.

The twins had an elder sister and two brothers, aged between eleven and eighteen, and their mother had also suffered a miscarriage and a still birth. Their father, an asphalter in a road gang, was anything but a gentle man. As a child Tricia was frightened of his strength and his outbursts of rage. She sought refuge in the garden where the trees became friends she could talk to. She would hug their trunks and stroke the flowers with her fingers. Swarms of mayflies bobbing up and down in the soft light were all tiny fairies in her world. She made small houses out of dock leaves for the fairies to live in.

Tricia's mother came from a generation in which people knew their place in society. Hers was a black and white world run by those whose education placed them firmly above her own working class. A doctor's diagnosis was never mistaken. Teachers were always right. The household was ruled by her husband, whose power was absolute, and who expected and got total submission from his wife.

Tricia was forbidden by her father to leave the garden. There were no holidays, no school outings and no family excursions to the seaside. She had no real friends at school – the other children called her 'Cod's Eyes'. Sex education passed her by completely and her ailing mother gave her no guidance about her body. Tricia's mother loved her children and cared for them, but the manner of their arrival in the world was a process which she could not bring herself to speak about to her sensitive daughter. For Tricia's mother sex was something to be endured. Giving birth to babies was so unclean and degrading that it was essential for a woman to be 'churched' afterwards. By the time Tricia left school at fifteen she had little knowledge and even less understanding of how a child was conceived.

When Tricia was eighteen her mother died. Tricia was mortified, and laid the blame on her father's ill-treatment of her. Fear turned to hatred, but she had neither the self-confidence nor the money to leave home, where she continued to live with her two sisters and her father. There was a man a few years older than Tricia who was kind to her and wanted to marry her. He was her first boyfriend, and though Tricia was uncertain about the feelings he roused in her, they married in September 1964 when Tricia was nineteen. Six weeks later she was pregnant with her first daughter. Their first home was a caravan in a field, and it was to this that she returned from the maternity hospital.

Having no contact with babies, no mother to turn to, and no neighbours to advise her, Tricia brought up her daughter by intuition and trial and error. Her only source of water was a standpipe fifty yards away along a muddy path. Despite the difficulties and hardships, Tricia was fastidious about cleanliness. The perfection of her baby's tiny body filled her with wonder. She adored her daughter and loved dressing her in pretty clothes. Tricia herself always dressed smartly and anyone seeing her proudly wheeling her pram in the town would never have guessed her circumstances.

By the time her next daughter was born three years after the first the family had moved into a house. When her third child, a boy, arrived two years later, Tricia's marriage was on the rocks. The break-up left her wounded and disillusioned. Her life was in ruins. She was raped and forced to live in accommodation for the homeless. Here she mixed with people trapped by poverty, many of whom could not cope in a consumer society.

A second marriage, to a man who drank heavily and who frequently beat her, was a disaster. To pay for the drink he sold her jewellery and anything else he could move from the house. Debts mounted until the electricity was cut off. When her husband threatened to kill her, she was terrified and slept with a knife under her pillow in the same room as her children. In winter, they were cold, often hungry, and lived by candlelight.

After a harrowing court case Tricia set about building a new life. Slowly she paid off her debts and moved her children into a council house. She lived on her nerves and a diet of sweet coffee and cigarettes, often eating only a slice of dry toast in a day. Tricia, by now a manic depressive, was known as a *prima donna* in the office where she worked because of her volatile temperament, but she was also a brilliant saleswoman. In 1982 her bank manager agreed to give her a loan to enable her to take herself and her two youngest children away for the first holiday they had ever had together. It was during that time in

Portreath that she met the dolphin Percy and discovered the very special healing love that only dolphins can give.

By observing her response to the dolphin I began to understand something of an interaction that I could never experience myself, for in many ways I was the very opposite of a manic depressive. Besides, in contrast to Tricia, when I first met Donald, the dolphin who was to change my life, I had a stable marriage and a united, loving family.

II

Bewitched by a Dolphin

The full film crew assembled in Solva on Friday, 9 August, and stood on the slipway at 9.30 a.m. just as it started to rain. The Force 8 wind was blowing straight into the harbour, where white horses reared on a dull grey sea. The planned sea voyage on the *Iolanthe* was abandoned.

We returned in sunshine at 2.30 p.m. The wind was still ferocious, though Jan was prepared to go to sea. The sound crew were put on stand-by. Colin Stevens, the director, decided he should attempt to film without sound some rough weather sequences that would cut into the material I had shot of Tricia in rough water round Black Rock. We set sail for the harbour entrance.

The water around Black Rock was churned up but we could see that it was wilder and even more spectacular around another rock called Green Scar, further out to sea. Further still was a half-exposed rock, Black Scar, where the sea was even more furious.

Jan knew that the rock dropped steeply into the sea on two sides. He steered the *Iolanthe* as close as he could to give us the best camera viewpoint. With her head into the wind the *Iolanthe* seemed to relish the prospect. As we came alongside Black Scar the boat climbed up a very large wave and crashed into the following trough like a bucking bronco. When we rose to the next crest I was able to look down on to two vicious, briefly revealed reefs that were pointing directly into the wind like the horns of a bull. The sea, running between the horns, had nowhere to escape and was forced up towards the fully exposed rocks, moving faster and faster as the water became shallower and shallower. Finally, the trapped foam exploded over Black Scar where the wind tore it to shreds and dispersed it in clouds of spume. Anything in the water caught between the horns of Black Scar would have been destroyed immediately. It was like being on a railway platform when an express train hurtles past. You know you are safe where you are, but a few feet away is instant death.

We were running straight into the wind. Mick, using a small camera inside a housing, filmed the scene which was momentarily obliterated from his view by a sheet of white foam. We slid through the crest of another wave that crashed into the wheelhouse in which we were standing and was deflected sideways into masses of glistening white spray.

Once we were past the rocks the motion of the sea eased a little. 'Let's run back along the other side,' said our intrepid cameraman.

Jan turned the boat round in a large semi-circle and started the run in. Now we had the wind behind us, and the motion of the boat was completely different. We were almost surfing, carried along on the crest of one wave as it passed before sinking like a lift into the succeeding hollow. If you've got the nerve and the power it is possible to ride such waves, remaining on their crests.

'Come on, Jan, give it some welly,' Mick yelled through the howling wind.

Almost keeping pace with the waves, we raced towards Black Scar which, locked in foam, appeared as lethal as a circular saw in motion. As we came alongside we were lifted to the top of one of the biggest waves to attack Black Scar that afternoon. Picking up speed, we rushed forward. The two horns of the treacherous reef showed themselves momentarily before trapping a section of the wave and funnelling it to destruction. Just outside the zone of imprisoned, tortured water the wave continued its crazy passage, and we hurtled forward on its crest. Then we tipped over the top. In the next instant the *Iolanthe* was rushing down the leading face of the wave like a toboggan down a steep hill. I looked astern and saw we were being followed by a near vertical wall of water which was being toppled by a following wind and was falling towards us. High above the transom in the middle of this oceanic escarpment was the inflatable we were towing. The wind snatched out a heavy milk bottle crate Jan used as a seat and flung it overboard. At that moment I thought we were doomed, and that the sea would come crashing over the stern and swamp us.

Jan pulled back the throttle as we plunged into the base of the trough. The boat shuddered from stem to stern and for a split second seemed undecided as to whether it was going to succumb to the sea. But the *Iolanthe* was a noble vessel. She reared heroically out of the raging foam and allowed the hissing wave to pass angrily on its way. By the time we rose on to the next crest we had been swept past Black Scar and were out of danger. I glanced at Colin Stevens, who had looked back at the same moment as me. I could see from the expression on his face that he was aware we had had a close call.

When we were safely back on shore and complimenting Jan on his skill as a seaman he smiled a rare, wry smile. 'Never look back, Horace. Never look back.'

It was good advice, in more ways than one.

Simo was young and growing up. He became very rumbustious at times. I enjoyed this behaviour and must confess that when he was with me I encouraged him. However some of those who got into the water with Simo were not good swimmers and were frightened by his antics. He also started nipping people with his sharp teeth — even Tricia. We were recording under-water sound when it first happened, and the recordist said the dolphin was making a sound like a child in pain. Colin Stevens received the same treatment as Tricia and left the water with his hand bleeding. When I got into the water with Simo, however, he stopped doing it for no reason we could fathom. All the same, the rumour going round Solva that night was that the dolphin had begun savaging the film crew.

This prompted us to produce a pamphlet which we distributed in Solva and displayed in the Harbour Master's office. In it we made the point that Simo was an adolescent wild male dolphin who could easily kill a human. We asked that his power be respected, and that all of those going into the water with him should remember he was not a cuddly toy.

For the vast majority of locals, and the many visitors who travelled to Solva, their meetings with Simo were totally joyful. One visitor described her feelings when she left.

> . . . the last sight I had of Simo was of that matchless looping through the water, as though he were being poured from air to water in one silken sinuous curve. Feelings of intense deprivation, and unbelievable joy, which are with me still.

There are many people who feel a very strong affinity with dolphins and a few for whom the attraction is so powerful that it changes their lives. They are compelled by an inner force to seek dolphins wherever they might be found. One such person is German-born Carola Hepp whom I met in New Zealand where we were both visiting a fellow cetacean enthusiast, Wade Doak. She moved to Cornwall to be close to Percy when he was frequenting the waters off Portreath, and she joined my expedition to Brittany where we filmed the dolphin Jean Louis for the television feature, *A Closer Encounter*. When Carola heard about Simo, she could not resist the mystic pull she felt towards Solva.

Tall, statuesque, and a superb swimmer, Carola is cosmopolitan, well-educated, conversant in several languages, and completely self-assured. She is a talented artist and musician, and writes poetry in English. Carola and Tricia are different in almost every respect, and perhaps because of this they have come to regard themselves as sisters. Yet, despite their opposite personalities and lifestyles, both experience a compulsive attraction towards dolphins – which Simo somehow satisfied.

The two often went in the water together, experimenting with ways of conveying their feelings towards Simo. They would lie on the surface of the sea, holding hands, their outstretched arms forming a circle. Sometimes they remained quietly like this, trying to project their thoughts and feelings through telepathy.

On one occasion they were joined by a delightful local girl, Joanna Roberts – known affectionately to us as Jo-Jo. Nine-year-old Jo-Jo was nervous of being in the water with Simo and so joined hands with Tricia and Carola. Quite spontaneously, the three began to chant. At first the sounds were discordant, but they quickly fell into a natural rhythm. The wailing sound they made was loud and appeared to cause the surrounding rocks to resonate. The air became charged with a feeling of excitement and expectancy, inducing a tension similar to that generated by ululating African tribal women gathered for a ritual. As I watched and listened I felt a prickling sensation on the back of my neck. Simo circled as if bewitched. Afterwards Carola said she had felt a brief period of profound spiritual communion with the dolphin.

Behaviour and observations like this were discussed at Anne Marks' house where gatherings of dolphin enthusiasts were held on several evenings. One of the people I met at these soirées was Steve McGruder, a black American hypnotherapist whose father was still a doctor in general practice at the age of ninety. Steve was quietly spoken and had dark penetrating eyes. Like dolphins, he was nomadic. He took very few possessions with him on his journeys and considered himself to be not an American, but a citizen of the world.

Steve joined a group on the *Iolanthe* one day and the usual frenzy of activity began as soon as Simo appeared. The dolphin followed us and stayed around while Jan anchored the boat in a cove out of the wind. Knowing that the dolphin could swim away at any time, most people kitted up immediately and jumped overboard. Not Steve McGruder, who retained his quiet dignity and got changed slowly. Unlike the rest of us who put on rubber suits to insulate ourselves, Steve wore only a pair of swimming trunks. He had a fine physique. When he felt the time was right, he slipped quietly into the water and showed not the slightest sign of feeling the cold.

I could see that Steve was one of those privileged people who Simo liked immediately. From the way the two of them behaved I sensed a mutual respect and a form of communication that was simpler than body language. When Steve stroked Simo with his hands, firmly yet gently, something mysterious seemed to pass between them. Ensconced in my wetsuit I slipped into the water to take some pictures. Simo much preferred the company of the near-naked swimmer and ignored me completely.

Steve McGruder stayed in the water for about thirty minutes. Later, when we were discussing the events of the day, he said: 'It's the quality of a meeting like that that matters more than the quantity.' There was nothing in his remark to denigrate me by implying that his relatively brief experience was comparable with the hundreds of hours I had spent with dolphins in the sea. None the less what he had said was a salutary reminder for those who fervently strive to amass more and more possessions and experiences.

This thought jumped into my mind a few days later when we had Jean Sayre-Adams, a nurse-healer from California, on the boat. It was a cold day and Simo had come into the harbour. Jean changed into a swimming costume and then climbed down the ladder over the stern of the *Iolanthe*. The cold gripped her abdomen like a vice and she gasped for breath as she lowered herself into the water. She held on to the ladder and stretched out her hand towards Simo and stroked him briefly as he swept past. She shut her eyes and quietly murmured, 'He touched me. He touched me.' It was as if she had been touched by God. For her it was a spiritual experience. She continued to cling to the back of the boat for several minutes, standing half-submerged, feet still on the ladder, eyes shut, her entire body trembling while her mind floated on another plane of existence.

Tricia, who had been suffering from a migraine attack, was not on the boat. When she met Jean later she took hold of her hands and the two of them were locked together by the bond of common experience. Jean was still quivering from her meeting

7-8 The wrecked tug provided a dramatic backdrop for the HTV
film *Bewitched by a Dolphin*, and it was from here that
Simo towed Tricia away on an unforgettable journey

9 Simo with Anne Marks (*left*), Jo-Jo Roberts, Tricia Kirkman
and Carola Hepp, all of whom fell in love with him

10 Simo with hypnotherapist Steve McGruder – one of the few not
wearing a wetsuit to get into the sea with the dolphin

with Simo. Tricia did not attempt to suppress the joy she shared with Jean and tears ran down their cheeks.

Jean's response to Simo was completely different to that of another American who went to Solva especially for the dolphin experience. She hired a small fishing boat, and took Tricia and me along at the invitation of the skipper. Simo came into the harbour and Tricia jumped in to keep the dolphin company.

When the American woman, who was extremely large, lowered herself into the water, Simo took little notice of her, whereupon she demanded that Tricia, who was obviously a distraction, should get out immediately. Even though she was now the only person swimming in the harbour, the very fat, rich, American lady got only fleeting attention from the dolphin – much to Tricia's barely concealed glee. Later, somewhat aggressively, she asked Tricia what all the fuss about meeting a dolphin was for. She had come to Solva for a magical experience and it had not happened. Patiently Tricia tried to explain what a lucky person she was, just to have seen Simo, let alone touch him. It was obvious that this particular visitor had her life tightly under control and could afford to buy her pleasures. Her expectations in this case, however, were completely unfulfilled – the water was cold and the dolphin inattentive. For her the visit to Solva was a complete waste of time and dollars.

The woman's attitude hurt Tricia's innate sense of justice and she became angry when she thought of all the people who would have benefited from just seeing Simo, but who couldn't afford to travel to Solva.

To most Americans who met Tricia fleetingly in Solva, she must have appeared a dizzy dame moonstruck about dolphins. The truth was that time spent with Simo was beyond any price for Tricia. One person to realise this was Garner Thomson, who arrived in Solva on 7 October 1985 to write an article for the South African *Sunday Tribune*. A gentle, sensitive and perceptive man, he understood immediately how important Simo was to Tricia, whom he described in his article as 'an eloquent vital woman, with the lean, dark, gypsy good looks of young Cher Bono'.

During his brief stay Garner found out that the harbour master, Sharkey Phillips, thought of Simo as the reincarnation of a dead fisherman friend, Nico, whose ashes were scattered on the sea at the place where he first met and befriended the dolphin. Sharkey was fiercely protective of Simo and the dolphin's right to first claim on the fish in the sea.

Garner also discovered that Anne Marks had been widowed two years previously after more than twenty years of marriage. When she first met Simo she was sixty and somewhat reserved, but she had spontaneously stripped off to her underwear and gone into the sea to meet the dolphin. Following this experience, she sold her house in St David's and moved to Solva where Simo helped her to reshape her life. When eventually she went back into the sea again with Simo, she said she felt a different person, describing it as a rebirth.

Halfway through his research Garner Thomson had his own dolphin experience. Simo put on a lively display when Garner entered the water, and the South African reported in his subsequent article how it felt to have Simo barrel past him like a dark grey torpedo:

> But then he (Simo) spots Tricia, with whom he has developed a moving and unique relationship, and sweeps underneath her, turning, wheeling, spiralling, lifting her, bearing her off in excited 50 metre dashes out to sea.

The day Garner went to sea off Solva was memorable not just for him, but for all of us on board Buzz Bland's little wooden fishing boat. It was a wild day, the sky dramatic and ever-changing. At times we were in bright cold sunshine, then we would see a squall approaching. Minutes later the sky was dark, the sea was grey and we were being pelted with needle-sharp rain. It went as quickly as it came and once again we found ourselves being warmed by the sun.

The sea was so rough we had to abandon underwater filming, but with the film crew perched high on the cliffs overlooking the scene we continued to work on the wrecked ship. I waited for the agreed signal indicating that Mike had finished shooting Tricia in the surf that was pounding over the ship's stern. When Colin stood on the clifftop with arms outstretched, like the statue of Christ at Rio de Janeiro, I knew the task was complete.

As Colin climbed into his car to return to Cardiff he said, 'The boat is paid for for the rest of the day. Why don't you and Tricia go out and play with Simo? I'll give you a call next week, Horace.'

Tricia and I jumped straight back into Buzz's boat. 'Take us to the archway,' I said to our boatman. We were not going to miss the opportunity for one last ride in a wild sea before we too returned home.

Tricia was now quite fearless when wearing her wetsuit. Even if the boat sank she knew that she could survive in the water, no matter how rough it was. Simo accompanied us all the way.

Despite the raging sea, the boat became relatively still in the lee of the Cathedral (as we called the natural rock archway). There the water was exceptionally transparent. It was close to high tide as waves came surging through the Cathedral. Tricia's sense of immortality infected me as I swam under the arch, falling and rising with waves that sometimes almost touched the roof. The descent was exhilarating, like going down in a fast lift between two sheer walls of rock. As the level fell the sea cascaded over the suddenly exposed ledges in seething waterfalls until the next wave rose rapidly again and swamped everything. All around us was the sound of crashing water. Sometimes it foamed over our heads, and once I was bumped hard against the rocks, though two layers of thick neoprene sponge in my wetsuit protected me from a painful bruising.

A year before Tricia would not have gone into a swimming pool; now here we were riding a maelstrom of water into which most experienced divers would not have ventured. The sky was grey. The sea was dark and forbidding. Rain started to pour down. We were experiencing the sea in one of its most violent moods, and all the time we had Simo for company.

When we had gone right through the archway, Tricia took hold of the dolphin's fin and he started to tow her away. I caught hold of her fins and Simo towed the pair of us in tandem. Eventually she let go and we had to make our own way back to the boat. Buzz was relieved when we reappeared through the archway – from his position we had disappeared completely under the cascading foam.

Simo kept closer to the shore on the way back to Solva. We saw him arch occasionally as he broke the surface perhaps 150 metres away. Tricia laughed as the boat climbed the mountainous waves, tottered on their tops and then thumped down into their troughs. A couple of times the water surged over the gunwales, but we knew we were immortal. Simo followed us almost to the jetty, then turned back to sea before Tricia had time to say goodbye.

She never saw Simo again.

We returned to Pembrokeshire the following April and discovered that the tug had been pushed much higher up the beach and on to rocks during the winter gales. Forty miles up the coast a local fisherman, Winston Evans, said he frequently saw dolphins in the area and took us out in his boat to them, but they were more interested in one another than in us. There was one pair, however, which always stayed close together but kept well away from the boat. We filmed them with a long telescopic lens from the shore.

Had Simo left Solva and found a mate? We never found out. But we liked to think so, and we had a perfect shot to end our film, *Bewitched by a Dolphin*. Colin commissioned music and lyrics for the film from the talented young composer Cathy Shostak, who attempted to capture Simo's bouncy personality. I was pleased with this bold approach because it represented a break from the style of music that it was customary to put over underwater film sequences.

When a film is completed there is always a lot of footage left over that remains unused. Sometimes exceptional material is omitted because, despite its quality, it does not fit into the story-line, or the continuity is wrong. Knowing that we were hoping eventually to help depressives, Dennis Pratt, the editor, collected some of these trims and in his spare moments put them together. One of the visuals showed Tricia being carried gently across the sea by Simo. He used the song 'Somewhere', by Barbra Streisand as a background. The lyrics convey the message that *somewhere* there is a place where everyone can find love and happiness.

For Tricia, that somewhere was Solva.

· 12 ·

The Great Gamble

When I had worked, as a young research scientist, on the relationship between the chemical structure of substances and their effects on the human body, leads had always come in the first instance from natural substances. This is still the case for almost all of the medicines in common use. The most widely used drug in the world, for instance, acetyl salicylic acid, or aspirin, originates in the bark of the willow tree. The green mould which grows on bread and cheese is called *Penicillium*, from which the antibiotic penicillin is isolated. Thus I have come to the view that nature holds the answer for the relief of, and even the cure for many human ailments, if only we can find the vital clue. If something as apparently insignificant and innocuous as a piece of mouldy cheese could eventually lead to the development of a wide range of antibiotics, saving countless lives, then I felt we should open our minds wide when looking to nature for help in treating depression, especially after the experience with Simo in Solva.

Ever since I first met Donald the dolphin off the Isle of Man in 1974 I had been assimilating circumstantial evidence to support the concept behind Operation Sunflower without realising it. I had seen the effect Donald had on Geoff Bold, the mechanic at the Penlee Lifeboat Station, who had been close to a nervous breakdown. I described in my book *Follow a Wild Dolphin* how the dolphin lifted the mechanic's depression, but did not appreciate the full significance of this observation at the time.

At the end of my film about Donald, *Ride a Wild Dolphin*,

I had said that the dolphin gave out an aura or emanation which made people joyful. I couldn't define it more precisely, but I knew it was there. As time went by I accumulated letters from people, some diagnosed by their doctors as depressives, others who just felt down for long periods, all of whom commented on the uplifting effect dolphins had upon them.

After giving a lecture in Belfast I received a letter from Rosie Drewitt who told me she had come to my film show at the end of a very depressing day. Among other things, her dog, which had been the family pet for many years, had died, and just seeing Donald on film caused her anxiety to disperse. She had gone away feeling at peace with the world.

There were also indications from outside my own orbit of experience which pointed to dolphins possessing special qualities. To the Minoans as far back as 1500 BC dolphins were symbols of joy and music. Living much closer to nature than we do in our era of post-industrial revolution, did the ancients know that the dolphins bestowed spiritual benefits upon humans? Was this why in ancient Greece dolphins were deified, so that to kill one was a crime punishable by death? Close examination of old myths and customs usually reveals a logical reason for their existence.

It was talking about dolphin-related topics like this during my film show at the Harbour House Hotel in Solva which prompted Bill Bowell's daughter to ask me to take him out to see Simo, and it was seeing Bill's response and hearing Tricia's comment about him blossoming like a sunflower that led me to the realisation that they were all connected to my theory that dolphins could help depressives.

When I left Solva at the end of filming, I was under no delusions as to the magnitude of the task. It was then that fate took a hand and laid out a pathway.

It started when the subject of keeping dolphins in captivity became an issue of such public concern that the government commissioned Dr Margaret Klinowska to prepare a review of the situation in the United Kingdom. After her report was published I joined in the debate and pleaded the case for dolphins to be left to enjoy their lives in freedom, in the open sea. I did a television interview early in 1987, literally in the harbour at Portreath, standing on the sea-bed when the tide had gone out. I was joined by Bill Bowell, who spoke with great sincerity about the effect a wild dolphin had had on him.

Not surprisingly, I received many letters via the BBC from depressives for whom conventional treatment and medication had failed. Some of them were pitiful and increased my awareness of just how debilitating depression really is. In many ways it is much more traumatic than other medical conditions where the symptoms are easy to distinguish, and the natural healing process, coupled with established treatments, can be expected to produce a favourable outcome within a predictable time. A person appearing in public with a limb in plaster can expect sympathy, but this is not so for someone with an injured mind. Indeed a depressed person is likely to be told to pull him- or herself together. Remarks such as 'It's all in your mind,' which trivialise the condition serve only to make the depressive feel still worse.

Someone with a broken leg can joke about it, might even encourage friends to adorn the cast with graffiti, so becoming the centre of attention. The opposite happens to the depressive whose condition often arises from an imagined need for love. They do not smile. Being in the company of a depressive can be difficult and boring, so they tend to be avoided. Rejection exacerbates the problem. On top of all this, the sufferer has no idea when, or indeed if, he or she will ever recover.

The most obvious symptom of depression is that of being in a state of emotional dejection, though the sufferer may well successfully conceal some depression-related behaviour. Such was the case with Jemima Biggs whose mother wrote to me after seeing the television interview with Bill Bowell and me in Portreath:

My daughter Jemima has suffered from depression and anorexia nervosa for five years or more and is caught up in a whirlpool of self-disgust from which there seems to be no escape.

She is almost twenty-one, very attractive, and used to be a bright spark and a wonderful natural swimmer. Now we see only glimpses of her former self, and watch anxiously as she struggles with her life as a student at the college of St Mark and St John in Plymouth, where she is doing an English degree with film and television studies.

She is extremely sensitive and responsive, and is told that she has healing powers herself, and I immediately felt that this intimate communication with the dolphin would break the pattern of her suffering – and ours.

Another person to contact me was Marie Jackson who told me that her twenty-three-year-old son, Neal, was suffering from what she called acute stress, which had gradually got worse. He did not believe in taking drugs for fear of getting hooked on them. There were times when the prospect of facing the day was so terrifying for Neal that his mother would have to get him up and dress him in the morning.

By the time I received these letters a plan was forming in my mind. First, I felt that these two mothers, who were very concerned about their grown-up children, should know a little more about my background and the circumstances that had led to my hypothesis. I sent them copies of my book, *Tale of Two Dolphins*, in which Tricia's interaction with Percy is described, and suggested that if they felt they would like to proceed further they should talk to Tricia, who had spoken sympathetically to Bill before he went into the sea with Simo. I also suggested that they should contact Bill and his wife, and told them about a friendly dolphin that I knew was cavorting with divers off the coast of south-west Ireland. I pointed out that I needed to work with a dolphin which sought human company, and such dolphins are rare. Furthermore when friendships are made they are often short-lived. Both Percy and Simo had stayed for only two years before disappearing completely. I was acutely aware that I would have to get the project going quickly.

Once again providence lent a hand. After I had given Jon Levy, an independent radio and television producer, a long interview for BBC Radio Humberside, he offered to talk to the directors of his public relations company, Wyke Farmer, about the considerable financial gamble of investing in a film which we would sell to a television station after it was finished. In that way we could keep control and avoid the hassle of bending our ideas to fit in with those of a sceptical television producer who might be forgiven if he found our plans somewhat far-fetched.

Jon also contacted Neil Faith, a cameraman with whom he had worked previously, and it was with Neil and his wife, Margot, that I went to Dingle in April 1987 for a reconnaissance. We took with us Rico Oldfield, whose job it was to take still pictures to back up Neil's video film.

It did not rain at any time from our departure on 23 April until our return on the 29th, which anyone who has been to the west of Ireland will appreciate is unusual. But then the whole trip had an element of magic about it. Everything worked in my favour: the weather was idyllic, the dolphin was co-operative, the scenery was magnificent and the people were as charming as only the Irish can be.

I was also inspired by the poet Heathcote Williams, who had given me a tape of himself narrating his epic poem *Whale Nation* shortly before its publication. One evening, as the sun was setting over Dingle Bay, I played the tape in my car and listened to Heathcote's rich voice extolling the virtues of the entire whale family, of which dolphins are members, and detailing how they were used and exploited after the industrial revolution to the point where they faced extinction. The poem carries the most powerful whale conservation message I have ever heard, and it raised in the four of us in that car a sense of wonder. As we listened we were aware that a short distance away, just beneath the lighthouse, was a small-toothed whale, order – *cetacea*, sub-order – *odontoceti*, super family – *delphinoidea*, family – *delphinidae*, sub-family – *delphininae*, genera – *tursiops*, species – *Tursiops truncatus*, who bore no grudge, or weapons, and was making overtures of unconditional friendship to any humans who would join him in the sea.

Who could refuse such an invitation? None of us.

When we left Ireland we were all looking forward to returning as soon as possible with Bill Bowell, Neal Jackson, Jemima Biggs, plus a full crew, to film the theory behind Operation Sunflower being put to the test.

· 13 ·

'A Big Splash for Mankind'

The effect of meeting a dolphin has been likened by some people to a religious experience. Certainly when Bill Bowell set out for Ireland in June 1987, it was for him an act of faith. He had said that his depression felt like being in a pit from which there was no escape, and was convinced that contact with the dolphin in Dingle Bay would cure his blues. Other depressives have used the same analogy, usually adding that only those who have suffered it can really know how utterly black life becomes. Perhaps the worst aspect of their state is that they become so pessimistic that they can see no hope of recovery. Bill's meeting with Simo off the Welsh coast had produced a tiny chink of light in his darkness.

At the same time, I was very conscious of the need for me to keep a completely open mind and be as objective as possible. I wanted the film to be an honest account of what took place. It seemed important for us to film what occurred as and when it happened, with the camera being as unobtrusive as possible. Reconstructions after the event would not do, but even so, we had to have a story-line. I produced a working script which began with Bill being introduced to the dolphin.

I was also anxious to avoid suggesting that I had been responsible for the Dingle dolphin's friendly attitude − credit for that belonged to the local people. An Irishman should make the introduction, I thought, and who better than Paddy Ferriter, one of the first to observe the dolphin and the build-up of its friendly attitude towards fishermen and divers.

Paddy was stubbornly independent, loved to talk and had a

wonderfully restrained sense of humour. He had found an enviable peace living alone in the isolated land-based light-house that guided the fishing boats into Dingle harbour. His job of lighting and maintaining the oil lamp ceased to exist when the electricity supply was connected to the white-painted cast-iron tower and the adjoining house where he lived. Paddy was made redundant by a photocell and an electric light bulb. However he was of retiring age and continued to occupy the house.

One of the few concessions Paddy made to technology in his personal life when the electricity was switched on was the acquisition of a television set. He was born on the Blasket Islands, and when asked what his parents would have thought of the contraption, he said they would have considered it 'the work of the Devil' and thrown it over the cliffs. Paddy was not impressed by the consumer society that arrived with the flick of a switch and he displayed a complete lack of greed. Rico, our photographer, took some pictures of him, and in return for Paddy's co-operation offered to send him a set of prints.

'Sure, what would I be doing with a whole set of photos?' he inquired. 'One will be enough.'

The only approaches to the lighthouse were along the cliff-top path from Beenbawn or across the fields from Dingle town two to three miles away. Paddy had not been to Dingle for six years and had no intention of going. If people wanted his company they made the effort to find him. Several friends and relatives had offered him a home closer to civilisation, but the old bachelor would not be lured away. He got up when he wanted and went to bed when he felt like it. The time shown by clocks in his house bore little relationship to Greenwich Mean Time. He ate only when he was hungry and relied mainly on one of his nephews to bring him potatoes and other food. He grew his own onions and had an ancient range that he fuelled with driftwood gathered from the beach.

The life Paddy had led was hard. As a young man he had known what it was like to spend days fishing in all weathers for a catch that would fetch a pittance when eventually it was landed. During the economic boom of the post-war years the standard of living in most Irish households changed dramatically, and sadly, some would say, many lost their charm and character. Paddy saw no reason to change his lifestyle and, despite many attempts by well-meaning neighbours, he stubbornly refused to modernise himself or his abode.

For all his resistance to change, Paddy had a sense of pride and cut his own hair when he knew we were going to film him. He also whitewashed part of the outside of his house.

It was obvious from the moment Bill and Paddy met that the two of them got on well together. In some ways there was common ground between them. Paddy had isolated himself physically from mankind, whereas Bill had done so mentally.

Bill was filmed walking across the fields and then talking to Paddy in the lighthouse. At last the moment came that Bill had longed for. The two men ambled outside and looked down on to the channel. In his own inimitably laconic way of speaking, and with generous gestures of his pipe stem, Paddy indicated the dolphin's territory. He told Bill the dolphin had not been seen at all that day.

As Paddy pointed out various geographical features to Bill, Mike Benison drove his Zodiac into view on the water below. Mike's appearance coincided with Bill asking Paddy the question uppermost in his mind – where was Dorad the dolphin most likely to be seen? Paddy indicated the entrance to the channel and said, 'That's where you'll see him.'

At that precise moment the dolphin surfaced exactly where Paddy was pointing. It was just a fleeting glimpse and then the dolphin was gone. Having spent hours fruitlessly looking for dolphins whenever he was beside the sea, Bill found his respect for Paddy's knowledge of the dolphin's habits greatly enhanced. When the dolphin jumped a few moments later in front of Mike's Zodiac, exactly as Paddy predicted he would, Bill's admiration knew no bounds.

Mike drove his inflatable to the foot of the cliffs beneath the lighthouse and Bill scrambled down to greet him. A few moments later Bill was in the rubber boat talking to the dolphin as it swam excitedly round, under, in front of and behind the Zodiac which Mike drove in tight circles and figures of eight in the middle of the channel.

Paddy watched the dolphin from the top of the cliffs while Bill's dream was coming true. After waiting and longing for a whole year he was close to a dolphin once again.

Before long Bill transferred to the *Tuna*, a small boat owned by Mike's father, Laurence. His mother Jeannie acted as crew and stewardess when it was used for cruising, or in our case filming. The *Tuna* had a good-sized cabin into which Bill disappeared with his wife Edna, reappearing moments later, his round, ruddy face dusted with the talcum powder he had used to ease his entry into a new blue wetsuit. He had never worn fins, mask or snorkel before. I explained how to use them while I fitted each item in turn. At last he was ready to go into the water for the ultimate experience. He sat on the gunwale with his feet hanging over the side and simply fell forwards to flop face down into the water. Dorad the dolphin was waiting there to greet him.

Bill lay on the surface of the sea, his arms extended, and spontaneously started to click his fingers. As usual, Dorad examined him first from behind before moving round to look Bill in the face. Once eye contact was made, the two locked on to one another. When this happened it was immediately apparent to those of us watching that this was no ordinary first meeting between man and dolphin. The two lay motionless on the sea, face to face, joined by an invisible bridge across which waves of pure emotion passed. I had never before seen a dolphin remain stationary for so long with one person.

Bill adapted immediately to the snorkelling equipment, and it transformed him. He could see under water through the mask, propel himself with his fins, and breathe, with his head submerged, through the snorkel tube. He could also speak through the mouthpiece, and from the moment he entered the water we could hear strange sounds emerging from the top of the tube, among which 'Dorad' was just intelligible.

When the dolphin eventually moved away, Bill went after

him, full steam ahead. I had been in the water to receive Bill when he launched himself off the *Tuna*, and I had filmed the exchange of feelings with Dorad, but Bill swam so fast I couldn't keep up with him when he went in pursuit of the dolphin. He was a well-built man with strong legs, and the power he derived from his fins was far greater than anything I could generate. Dorad seemed to relish the idea that this novice (who had suffered a heart attack twelve years earlier) could outswim his instructor on his first snorkel in the sea.

When finally I caught up with them, the dolphin shunned me and gave all his attention to Bill. I reconciled my wounded pride with the thought that clearly I wasn't being an intrusive influence in my own experiment. I could film the pair inter-acting without changing it.

Bill was overjoyed with the attention he received from the dolphin. For him it was a momentous day. Over supper in the Armada Inn that evening this man of few words found his own way of expressing it. 'A small splash for man – a big splash for mankind.' For the first time he climbed out of the black bog of depression into which he had fallen twelve years previously.

The magic started to unfold at 10.30 a.m. next day after we had loaded the *Tuna* at the quay in Dingle and were following the deep water channel diagonally across the harbour to the cutting beneath the lighthouse that led to the open sea. We all felt excited, as if we stood at the threshold of a new golden age. No signs of ugly industrialisation could be seen anywhere. We were in the middle of a vast panorama of rounded hills, sculptured by the sunlight and decorated with the moving shadows of cotton wool clouds that drifted across an azure sky. Patchwork fields patterned the hillsides with subtle shades of green that changed continuously according to the light. Looking back from the lighthouse, we saw the Toytown houses of Dingle nestling in a valley beyond a sparkling expanse of water, with the church spire rising like a grey spear above the small oblongs of colour that lined the waterfront. Behind it soared the magnificent ancient brooding mountains of the Dingle Peninsula.

The dolphin did not appear at the spot where he had the previous day. With Mike Benison acting as boatman, Bill and I clambered into the Zodiac to search further afield. We did not have to go far. As we swung round the headland towards the open sea Dorad came bounding across the water to greet us. Having gained the dolphin's company we felt fairly confident he would stay with us. We took the inflatable along the coast and into the fissures that cut deep into the magnificent headland. Much to our delight, Dorad followed us wherever we went. The water was clear, and where it was shallow we could see his steel grey body moving like an animated submarine over the olive green kelp beneath us.

On the point of the headland was a large cleft in the rocks, and I decided to bring the *Tuna* to this location, which eventually became known to us as the Magic Cave. It was a natural auditorium with rocks hanging like curtains over the innermost recess that was our stage. I put on full diving gear and explored it, filming at the same time with a small Sony 8 video camera in its underwater housing. The tide was rising and the fishing boats that had been in the harbour during the weekend went past on their way to the fishing grounds. Under water I could hear the throb of their engines and was not surprised that I saw little of the dolphin, knowing how he liked to escort the ships that were passing through his territory. However, when Bill entered the water, the dolphin lost all interest in the ships and stayed with us.

Bill had swallowed a lot of water the previous day and choked a couple of times, still unaccustomed to using the snorkel tube. As his confidence and capability under water increased, so did the dolphin's activity around him, and there was a gradual increase in excitement both in the water and on board the *Tuna*, where cameraman Neil Faith was filming the onlooker's view.

When Neil wanted a new viewpoint, Mike Benison ferried him and his heavy camera and tripod to the rocks, where he helped him set up to film the action that was building up by the minute. I could sense the dolphin's adrenalin rising as he began circling faster and faster. I surfaced just as he exploded out of the sea, flew in a high arc and crashed back down, creating a wave that rushed into the back of the cave where it was trapped in the hollows, producing loud gurgles.

Encouraged by cheers from the boat and the camera crew on the rocks, Dorad launched himself high into the air four times more, setting up a confusion of waves in the restricted gulley that set Bill and me bobbing up and down like fishing floats in rough water. Before his energy was burnt out the dolphin rushed across to Bill on the edge of the circus ring where this amazing display of aqua- and aerobatics was taking place, reared over his shoulder and dived head-first back into the sea beside his chest. I was close by and filmed with the compact video camera the tangled turmoil of a dolphin rearing time and again around the startled snorkeller who often vanished from my view in a flurry of foam. It was exciting to watch, and even more exhilarating to be in the thick of it. Throughout the entire performance Dorad seemed to have complete control, and Bill trusted him, flowing with the action. As a result Bill came to no harm whatever, as he might well have done had he panicked and tried to escape.

Quite suddenly everything became uncannily quiet and still. We waited expectantly for whatever might happen next. But nothing did. Dorad's energy was spent and he swam swiftly away. The dolphin, in complete command as always, had decided the show was over.

When Bill went back in the sea again in the afternoon, you would not have known he was with the same dolphin. Dorad was in a passive, lazy mood. When Bill lay on the surface with his arms outstretched, clicking his fingers, the dolphin swam up to him until the two of them were face to face once again. Instead of explosive excitement a very gentle peace prevailed. Knowing what had happened just a few hours before, it would have been easy to interpret the body language as the dolphin acknowledging to Bill that he had tested him, and that the experience they had shared on a high physical and emotional plane had strengthened the bond between them.

We filmed Bill when eventually he swam back to the boat. 'How was it, Bill?' Jon Levy asked him.

Bill held on to the hand rope at the side of the Zodiac, leaned his head back, shut his eyes as if in a state of bliss, and paused before speaking.

'I cannot put into words what Dorad has done for me down there,' he said. 'I wish I could become a merman and stay here for ever.'

Bill did not really have to use words to express the feelings written so clearly on his face, and when a clip of the interview was shown later at the International Festival of Underwater Films in Brighton, many people in the audience were moved to tears.

· 14 ·

Eye to Eye with Jemima

Jemima's problems began when she was just ten years old and became aware of her own mortality. The deaths of her uncle and great-grandmother were extremely distressing for her and she grew desperately afraid of death and fire, so much so that she became alarmed if her parents lit a fire and she was not present to make sure it was safe. She spent much of her time writing morbid poetry.

When Jemima was sixteen she had a boyfriend and went on a diet to please him, losing five pounds in weight. Then her godmother died, and Jemima ate to comfort herself, putting back on the weight she had lost. After her boyfriend returned from a holiday abroad the relationship ended. But unlike other girls in similar circumstances, Jemima could not throw off the feeling of dejection that always comes with the end of a first love. She imagined it was because of her weight and began to diet, cutting out bread and cereals and increasing her consumption of high fibre foods such as fruit and vegetables. Jemima's feelings of rejection were compounded by the fact that she felt she could not return to her old friends because she had neglected them when she was with her boyfriend. For a time she buried herself in her college work, and her teachers confidently predicted she would get extremely good grades. The high hopes they had for one of their star pupils faded when Jemima stopped attending the college regularly. With both of her parents out working as teachers Jemima took to eating huge quantities of food and then making herself sick when she was alone in the house during the day. Her parents were not aware of this behaviour, but they and her teachers at college were concerned about Jemima's lack of work and arranged for her to see a child guidance counsellor. Jemima agreed to undergo hypnosis to calm her nerves.

She took time off college 'to pull herself together', but she failed disastrously. She started taking huge quantities of laxatives and still vomited after eating. She resorted to excessive exercise, in order to wean herself off the laxatives, and stayed up day and night. Her weight dropped from 8½ stone to 5 stone, but even so she felt excessively big and wore large clothes to hide her body shape. The appetite-enhancing qualities of the anti-depressants she then took caused her weight to rise sufficiently for her to be able to visit a penfriend in Italy. While she was away, however, her weight dropped back down again.

When she was twenty Jemima started a degree course in Plymouth which compelled her to leave home. She did not mix socially with students of her own age, but made friends with a few of the mature students on her course. She refused to see the psychiatrist while at college, but was helped by her college nurse and her landlady. When she arrived in Ireland she had just completed her second year and weighed 6½ stone. Yet in her own mind Jemima was excessively obese and felt 'like a sack of potatoes'.

Jemima arrived at the Armada Restaurant in Dingle at the end of what had been a wonderful day for us, and we were all in high spirits. She did not engage in the laughter and light-hearted banter that prevails on such occasions. We talked to her, and Bill made a special effort to raise her spirits. She always responded politely but continued to view the proceedings with a serious expression through the circular gold rims of her John Lennon-style spectacles. She ate nothing while we feasted, but sat huddled in the corner, knitting a pullover in dark green wool for her grandfather.

Comfortably settled into her room, with its view across fields to the harbour and the lighthouse, Jemima did not trust anyone to prepare food for her, and next morning ate half a grapefruit privately before I arrived to take her to meet the dolphin. We filmed Jemima boarding the *Tuna* and setting off to find Dorad who was waiting for us beneath the lighthouse. As the weather conditions were suitable we returned to the place we had visited the previous day and moored just outside the gulley leading to the Magic Cave.

The skipper's wife Jeannie, who had been a nurse, took Jemima into the cabin where, amid a jumble of diving bags and photographic equipment, she helped her change into a new cerise-coloured wetsuit, which added a little extra thickness to her matchstick limbs.

Part of Jemima's problem arose from the fact that she was a compulsive accomplisher. This trait in her character held her in good stead for meeting the dolphin because it made her determined to master the use of snorkelling equipment and overcome any other difficulties that might beset her. At school she had become a competitive swimmer and her competence showed itself immediately she joined Bill in the water. She let out no cry of anguish when the cold sea flooded into her wetsuit, which did not fit snugly. Watched and encouraged by Bill she swam forward, waiting for the magic moment. The dolphin meanwhile was busy examining her fins – a fact of which she was unaware at first because of the tunnel vision imposed by her facemask.

Warm and comfortable in my semi-dry wetsuit I watched Jemima's encounter with the dolphin through the viewfinder of an underwater camera, which to some degree detached me from the reality of the situation. This is how Jemima herself described her experience in an article called 'Depression and Anorexia' which she later wrote.

In order to enter the cold waters from the Atlantic we each had to don wet-suits. For someone who is intensely aware of her own body-shape this was quite an ordeal in itself because it made me feel absolutely enormous, but the shock of the cold water quite took my breath away. Once I found that I could use the mask and snorkel I began to forget the attention of cameras and switched to a different level of self awareness which hardly included my physical being. I became conscious of my body merely as an initial point of contact with the dolphin as he nudged his way up my body from behind and below me. Even this level of physical awareness dissolved, however, when I made my first eye-to-eye contact with him. From the look in that one eye which I could see as he contemplated me, I knew that it was he, not I who was in control of the situation. For someone who has not encountered Anorexia it is important to explain at this point that if Anorexia can be said to be about one thing in all cases, it is about control. The loss of control is devastating for the anorectic and this accounts for the common 'symptom' of a marked withdrawal into an ever smaller world which can be encompassed and controlled by the anorectic. Knowing this, perhaps other people can begin to see how very important that first encounter was. The acknowledgement of my lack of control in the meeting was felt deep within me but it was not alarming.

The dolphin seemed to be looking into my soul. He looked at ME – not my physical form, not my 'intelligence' or academic achievement – but ME. I realise that this was precisely what I have lost touch with. I have become used to measuring ME by external factors as the mechanism of society pressures me to do. The problem for the anorectic is that she takes these pressures too seriously and sets targets so high that failure is inevitable. When this occurs she cannot forgive herself. Dieting thus becomes both the process to an impossible target and the punishment for falling short. In this process I lost sight of a sense of where I was, what I wanted and how I felt. Food was my obsession and my phobia. As I saw what it was doing to my family as well as the manner in which I behaved I became alternately crippled by guilt and filled with anger at them. How could I have anything but low self-esteem! But here was a creature in the cold waters of Dingle Bay interested in and gentle towards that part of me so hurt and neglected.

*

When she first became aware of the dolphin's presence Jemima forgot about the cold. When she started to feel chilled I judged it was time for her to leave the water and restore her lost heat in the cabin of the *Tuna*.

Leaving Jeannie and the others on the *Tuna* to look after Jemima, Bill and I stayed in the sea, playing with the dolphin whose games became progressively more vigorous. A new one which I enjoyed was lying supine in the water with my legs tightly together and my fins projecting in a V formation into the air. Dorad put the tip of his beak against the notch between my heels and pushed hard, propelling me head-first through the water at considerable speed. On my back, and looking up at the sky, I could not see where I was going and trusted he would not ram me on to the rocks, which thankfully he did not. Dorad's behaviour was indicative of the new ground he was breaking in the build-up of contact and trust between us.

The film crew went off to work elsewhere after lunch leaving the party on the *Tuna* free to engage in developing dolphin-human interactions further still, without the intrusion of an underwater camera. This enabled those not directly involved with the film to join in the fun in the sea. These included Madeleine Harmsworth, who was reporting on Operation Sunflower for the *Sunday Mirror*. She had a special interest in the project because she had spent a month at the Warneford Hospital in Oxford, where Bill was being treated for depression. Madeleine's stay in the mental hospital was the result of a nervous breakdown when preparing for her university finals. Madeleine had since carved a successful career for herself in the competitive world of Fleet Street journalism. Her quiet smiling presence on board provided compelling evidence that it was possible to escape from the kind of small dark world into which Jemima had locked herself. The fact that Jemima was considering writing as a career when she graduated added to the common ground between these two articulate, intelligent and sensitive women.

Part of Jemima's withdrawal process was to avoid social occasions, yet in Dingle she was swept along with the tidal race of events in which we all participated. After her first meeting with the dolphin she encountered a group of singers and musicians performing traditional Irish music in the Star pub. Grey-haired farmers and fishermen wearing cloth caps sat alongside bright-eyed girls with skins as soft and fair as rose petals, all joining in the singing or listening in silence to the plaintive notes of a violin, or the Gaelic song about an unforgotten hero who gave his life during the turbulent days of 'the troubles'. You did not have to understand the lyrics to sense the deep dark streams of emotion it tapped into in that crowded, shadowy smoke-filled room, suffused with its thick yellow light. Bill, avuncular, his broad cheeks glowing red from the sun and the sea air, sat puffing at his pipe with his wife and sweetheart Edna nestled beside him; Madeleine, her dark hair pulled back off her forehead, smiled through eyes that glowed like coals; while Jemima, looking vulnerable and watchful, holding back, showed the merest trace of a crack forming in the barrier she had erected around herself.

It had been a long day for Jemima, emotionally and physically. At first I had to draw conversation out of her, but gradually I learned that she loved her family, especially her brother Rufus, who were all very talented, and she felt unable to live up to their expectations for her. By the end of the evening our exchanges were free flowing. Already it was possible to see a change taking place in her. When eventually we parted company, she told me she wanted to duck dive into the dolphin's world the following day.

She is still setting herself targets, I thought to myself, but perhaps that will be a substitute for her resolution not to eat. All I had seen her consume throughout the entire day were several cups of black coffee, without sugar, which was certainly not enough to replace the calories she had burned up since her grapefruit breakfast.

· 15 ·

Heathcote and Neal

The next person to arrive in Dingle was the poet and playwright Heathcote Williams. Although I had invited him to join the group, he arrived unannounced. He had bought a wetsuit and snorkelling equipment before leaving England, but had not tried them out. So excited was he when the dolphin appeared, he kitted-up immediately and rushed into the sea from the shore. In the circumstances he coped well. Afterwards he remarked that the legs of his wetsuit felt strange. It was not surprising, I told him, for in his haste to get in the water he had put on the long-johns back to front. The stiff strengthening pads, which should have been protecting his knees, were round the back of his legs.

Heathcote was a walking paradox. He had a head of long curly black hair and bought his clothes at Oxfam. He looked like a hobo, yet he had a deep, rich cultured voice. From afar his Chaplinesque appearance falsely conveyed the image of a person of little significance; close contact revealed dark hypnotic eyes and a powerful presence. Heathcote was shy in the company of strangers, an unusual trait in someone who counted professional acting among his occupations. He had no time for fools or charlatans, and made this perfectly clear. He was not materialistic, had strong views on moral questions, adhered scrupulously to his own sense of justice and was uncompromising in living by it.

I first struck up a friendship with Heathcote after hearing him recite a poem about elephants at the Elephant Fayre in Cornwall in 1981. It was an extraordinary gathering in the grounds of Port Eliot House where over 500 entertainers from all over Britain gathered to present music, theatre, dance and comedy. In addition there were craft displays and what were billed in the programme as 'stimulating talks'. That's where I came in, for I had been invited to take part in what was called *The Great Rainbow Debate*, a rural Speaker's Corner in which scientists and sociologists, writers and psychiatrists, agitators and astronomers gathered to debate topics which included the motor car, fringe medicine, and the education system. We also discussed questions as: did life come from outer space? are we descended from apes? does the state tell us all we need to know? is nuclear power a good idea?

For me, the most memorable event took place at midnight when the noise of the rock groups was overwhelmed by the amplified sound of an elephant trumpeting. It echoed across the lawns and caused everyone to look for its source. In the same instant Port Eliot House was flooded with yellow light, which revealed an enormous inflated elephant's head from which sounded the poem, read by its author Heathcote Williams. I was transfixed by the eloquence of the case he presented on behalf of the elephants, as he related example after example of how inhumanely mankind had exploited these enormous yet gentle creatures which possess the largest brain of any of the land mammals. He opened my mind to the fact that what we had done to the elephants had a close and equally unforgivable parallel in our treatment of the largest brained animals in the sea – namely the whale family which included my beloved dolphins.

Little did I realise then that six years later I would be escorting the poet into the Armada Inn in Dingle to meet a film crew and three people suffering as a result of the way in which we all exploited one another.

When I asked Heathcote if he would come to Dingle – or more accurately urged him to come – I thought he might find it interesting, and even stimulating to look into the eye of a dolphin roaming freely in the sea. Would the penetrating mind of the poet perceive and put into words that elusive quality which I called the 'spirit of the dolphin'? I did not expect him to become directly involved with the patients themselves, the third of whom, Neal Jackson, arrived in Dingle on the same day as Heathcote. Yet he added his own special ingredient to their experiences.

He set them at ease on their first meeting in the Armada Restaurant by taking out a pack of cards, tearing holes in the middle of four of them and magically stringing them together. He then produced a set of clubs and put on a juggling perform-ance, which finished with him offering to teach our would-be TV stars his skills. It was a happy occasion, yet who would have dared to imagine the outcome of our gathering together to engage with the mind of a dolphin, each in his or her own way? Certainly I could not foretell that Heathcote Williams would publish so moving an evocation of his encounters as he did later in a poem he called *Falling for a Dolphin*.

The next morning it was Neal's turn to be filmed making contact with the dolphin. In many ways Neal was the opposite of Jemima, whose troubles arose partly through her strength of character and her resolution to succeed at any cost. Her targets became obsessions. Neal did not lack strength of char-acter (he refused to take drugs to cure his depression) yet barriers kept pushing themselves up in front of him which prevented him from attaining what was expected of him. He had resigned himself to failure, but hated himself for doing so. Having imagined that everything and everybody was conspir-ing against him – that is precisely what happened. At school the other children picked up on his weaknesses and bullied him. As a laboratory technician he was derided by some of the staff, making him feel worse and pushing achievement even further away. Even his shoelaces seemed to conspire against him by coming undone. When people pointed this out to him, which they frequently did, he would retort, 'They're Bolshie shoelaces.' This humorous touch of self-ridicule indicated that he was aware of what some regarded as his stupidity, but his mental attitude made him powerless to do anything about it.

We decided that Neal should meet the dolphin by entering the water from the beach near the lighthouse. Like his two predecessors, Neal had worn neither fins, mask, snorkel, nor a wetsuit before. I gave him instructions in their use before he waded into the sea. From previous meetings I knew he was desperate to be seen to succeed. The opportunity to be seen on television was a great spur to him. Quite naturally he wanted to be seen to be masterful. But then, as usual, things went wrong.

I had gone to considerable pains to make sure his fins fitted properly, but they came off. Then the buoyancy of his wetsuit altered his stability in the water. He found he rolled around uncontrollably and could not swim well. Finally, when he saw a fin 200 metres away and heading towards him, he freaked out completely.

One result of his experiences in life was that Neal did not trust people. When he saw a grey torpedo shape hurtling towards him, he thought suddenly that I must be completely mad and had lured him into the sea maliciously. There was just one word uppermost in his mind – JAWS. He was terrified, and panicked. To make matters worse, water came pouring in through the mouthpiece of his snorkel tube and he started to choke.

Fortunately a fishing boat left the harbour at this stage and Dorad the dolphin departed to inspect it, leaving Neal, cold and frightened, to wade back to the beach with his escort.

He did not want to admit to me in front of the cameras that he was scared stiff. He pointed out to me that there were no spigots on the mouthpiece of his snorkel tube. I sympathised with his plight and became angry when I discovered that he had been given a faulty tube.

'Christ,' I said, 'no wonder you've had trouble. I couldn't use a snorkel tube like that. Who the hell gave it to you?'

The next time he went in I made sure that Neal had a proper snorkel tube, but after a short time he started to splutter and choke again. Once more he complained that the snorkel tube was leaking. When I examined it I found that one of the spigots was missing and the other was hanging on by a thread. So terrified had he been the previous day that he'd bitten right through the rubber grips in his mouthpiece and swallowed them without noticing it.

The problems that always seemed to impose themselves on Neal's life were now beginning to affect me. If Neal was incompetent in the sea, how could I possibly achieve my own objective – to assess what effect the dolphin was having on him? To add to the drama, we flooded a camera. Tension heightened noticeably in Dingle harbour.

The suppressed anguish of the day was finally dissipated that evening in the Armada restaurant when Heathcote made a spectacular entrance, juggling with three Indian clubs as he walked in through the open door. The level of merriment rose even further when news came through that Jemima had passed all her end-of-year exams with flying colours.

Neal and Jemima both came from comfortable middle-class homes and had no experience of what life was like on the wrong side of the tracks. Living rough, to many people with their type of backgrounds, was not having hot water coming out of the appropriate tap. That night they discovered from a large, powerful, rough-looking man who wandered into the Armada that Heathcote knew a great deal about the lives of down-and-outs.

The name of the tramp-like character who imposed his company on us was Martin Eagan. He drank only tea and declined the wine we offered him, telling us that he was a reformed junkie who had spent time in jail as a result of violent conflicts with the law. Indeed this was the condition he was in when he knew Heathcote over a decade earlier. Heathcote was surprised to see the stranger, and had assumed Martin to be dead because of the low state he was in when they last met. Martin, for his part, had not expected to meet Heathcote whom he had last seen running a squatting agency in London, where he had once found Martin a place to sleep with a group of homeless people. To protect themselves against bailiffs employed by the Church Commissioners, the squatters nailed an iron bedstead to the window and connected it to the mains electricity.

Neal found this highly amusing. It also gave him another perspective on life. It was the first time he had had a close personal encounter with someone like Martin – an articulate, intelligent dropout with a rich vocabulary, who cared nothing for whether his shoelaces were tied or not.

When the meal was over, I drove Martin to the house where he lived rent-free thanks to the typically Irish generosity of a local farmer. There he lit a fire, fuelled partly with dry dung. Over a cup of tea, and in the company of Heathcote, I listened to Martin play the guitar while he sang a song he had written about the dolphin. He also showed me his library of poetry books, many of them in Irish. These he bought with the proceeds of busking during the short tourist season in the summer. He read them in winter, when he wrote much of his own poetry while living on the dole. Martin mined his lyrics from a mountain of personal emotional experiences, and hoped that one day they might bring him fame and fortune.

It was 2.30 in the morning before Heathcote and I eventually retired to our respective beds. On the drive back to Dingle we were both quiet, lost in thought. Heathcote had made an unexpected link with a past period in his life, during which he helped literally thousands of helpless and often difficult people to combat the problems of homelessness and poverty in a city overflowing with wealth. London was where I was born, but that night it felt as distant as the moon.

One of the landmarks in Dingle harbour is a relic of the famine years of the 1840s. It is a derelict tower, built by Edward Hussey, and known as Hussey's Folly. According to the guide books, its construction provided employment during those difficult times. The hollow shell of the rectangular red sandstone building still stands on a rise overlooking the harbour and there is evidence of a fireplace on the first floor. A local historian told me that, when the building was first constructed, the owner used it as a library where he would sit, enjoy the view, and read his books. Then with a nod and a wink he added that it was also a convenient place for the highly respectable benefactor to entertain a certain lady friend. The ghost of Edward Hussey is said to walk through the ruin on dark nights, but nobody can tell if the trace of a smile on his face is due to his clandestine meetings with his mistress or Irish make-believe for the benefit of tourists.

Near Hussey's Folly are some much more recent ruins. These are in a secluded and sheltered bay near the lighthouse. Now all that remain of these edifices of an age of greater modesty are the concrete bases upon which they stood, and it was here, out of the wind and in the sun, that those not immediately involved in filming gathered on the morning following our late-night session with Martin Eagan. It was a relaxing place, and as we sunbathed Heathcote offered to continue with the juggling lessons.

We all lined up in front of our teacher. A bag of oranges was produced and each person was given three with which to practise. That left only one for our instructor, who picked up two dead jellyfish from the beach and demonstrated with them instead.

Later in the day we saw common jellyfish pulsing through the water with rhythmic contractions of their transparent umbrella-shaped bodies which were patterned with threads that seemed to glow with a pale, neon-blue light. Alive, under the sea, with their feathery tentacles trailing beneath them, they looked as delicate, beautiful and vulnerable as exotic flower blossoms. Out of the water they were cruelly transformed into lifeless shapeless blobs of jelly that became leathery as they dried out. Thinking about the ill-fated jellyfish, whose lives depended on the whims of wind and tides, it seemed to me that the chances of being thrown out by human society were just as random. Any one of us could find ourselves suddenly in the place of Neal, Jemima or Bill through circumstances outside our control.

11 All of the friendly solitary dolphins I had known enjoyed
playing with canoeists; the Dingle dolphin was no exception

12-13 Jemima Biggs, who suffered from *anorexia nervosa*, found that 'the experience was one of mutual love and trust which perhaps only another intelligent species like the dolphin can provide'

Approaching Nirvana

I am an extremely fortunate person. I have travelled extensively to exotic places. I have often slept under the stars on a beach beside a tropical sea, and have even been shipwrecked in the Philippines. Yet nowhere else have I found the mysterious qualities of south-west Ireland. When I awoke on Monday, 6 July 1987, and looked out of my window in the O'Connor farmhouse in Dingle, I felt as though I were in heaven, witnessing from on high the tranquil birth of a new and wonderful day. The ash tree beside the window was bathed in the mellow early morning light. Its leaves caught a stray, momentary wisp of wind, trembled slightly, and then became motionless again. The dark green fuchsia hedge that bordered the long lane leading down the incline to the road was delicately dusted with deep red blossoms. Beyond that the sea was as smooth as a woodland pond. Overhead a lonely seagull drifted lazily across a soft sky patterned with high fleecy clouds. A cow mooed, then all was silent again − an utterly all-pervading, peaceful quiet that invaded my soul.

My early morning reverie was a prelude to a memorable day for all three of the special people with whom I shared it, but for whom the world was not such a friendly and pleasurable place as it was for me. Once again we boarded *Tuna* and headed for the Magic Cave. The camera crew had been out hours before us, but there had been no sign of the dolphin, who did not appear even when we anchored. So, with Neal and Jemima, we set off in the Zodiac to see if we could find the elusive Dorad, passing the massive towering cliffs and the gullies and caves chiselled into them that could only be explored when the sea was calm.

The sheer magnitude and magnificence of the rocks, with their million-year history, always made me feel like a speck of humanity in a nano-second of time. I loved to talk to the cliffs and feel their presence especially when I was enveloped by the walls of the largest of the caves which opened into a dark, high-sided canyon flooded with still deep-green sea water. Nearby was a near-vertical wall of smooth rock that rose to a curved apex, which, from below, seemed to reach up and touch the sky. It was altogether a natural formation, but could have been the end wall of a temple. The fishermen, who had names for all of the local geological formations, called it the Tailor's Iron because it looked like the flat base of a giant iron standing upright.

The dolphin did not appear until we had circled Crow Rock, which stood guarding the entrance to the channel beneath the lighthouse. Having induced the dolphin to join us, we did not head straight back to the *Tuna* but retraced our path, Mike steering the inflatable into each of the caves in turn while I appraised them as possible filming locations.

One site that appealed to me was an archway in a rock wall well round the headland and out of sight of the lighthouse. Much to my delight, Dorad followed the inflatable through the narrow tunnel which opened into a cave. It was a perfect arena for filming, with the light striking it at a right angle. Also the water appeared to be clearer here. We would stay in this exposed location for as long as the good weather lasted – providing, of course, the dolphin stayed too!

Once again I filmed under water before the human stars of the film came into the sea. The high cliffs created sharp shadows that divided the undersea world into two. In the sunshine everything was bright and the water felt warm and inviting. The moment I swam into the shade the sea felt much cooler, although the temperature was exactly the same, and that extra sparkle, which made such a difference to the images recorded in my mind and on the film, vanished instantly.

Hanging in the shadow and looking out into the sunlit zone was like being in the auditorium of a darkened theatre and viewing the stage ablaze with light and colour.

One of the images I wanted to capture on film was that of the three depressives floating on the surface and holding hands to form a circle. If the dolphin was giving out some form of energy, I hoped it would be picked up by at least one of the three human aerials and then fed into the circuit of linked arms. Filmed by me from directly underneath, and also at the same time by the camera crew above the sea, I wanted to create a visually appealing star-shaped pattern which we could show from both sides. Furthermore I could make it spin on the screen by rotating the camera with the shutter running. It was an ambitious shot to attempt with three novices, especially as Neal was still nervous in the water.

Neal, who was very thin, quickly grew cold in the water and returned to the *Tuna* where his minder – a happy-go-lucky, burly, rugby-playing Lancastrian named Chris – helped him out of his diving gear. The rest of us stayed in the water, where something totally unexpected took place. Dorad spoke to me through his blowhole. The dolphin lay on the surface facing me and started to make sounds – 'awiss, awiss, awiss' – which those watching near by swore were his attempts to pronounce my name as most people did – 'Horis'.

It was the last day of Jemima's visit and she was determined to make the most of it. I had provided her with sponge-rubber gloves, as well as a wetsuit, for extra insulation, but they denied her the experience of feeling the dolphin's skin. She removed one of her gloves and gently caressed Dorad with her naked fingers. It was, she said, like stroking slightly oiled, smooth rubber, which gave almost imperceptibly to the touch, and was quite unlike the feel of a fish.

Just before it was time for Jemima to leave us and return to Dingle, Dorad gave what she called 'a final salute of farewell'. It was an electrifying display. Dorad circled the perimeter of the cave, thwacking his tail on the surface of the sea as he went. The effect was like gunfire, and he fired ten rounds in quick succession, each of them cracking with the impact and then booming as the trapped sound bounced off the encircling cliff walls.

As Mike sped away with Jemima in the inflatable, Dorad jumped right over the speeding Zodiac, causing him to duck instinctively for fear of being knocked on the head. He need not have worried. The flying dolphin cleared him with plenty of headroom.

The dolphin was following the inflatable when it returned. We spent the rest of the day enjoying his company while Jemima, back ashore, was being filmed sitting on the bed in her room and writing up her diary.

Towards the end of the afternoon I urged Neal to have another swim with the dolphin. I knew that I was pressuring him, and he yielded. Big Chris helped him to get kitted up. Bill took hold of both Neal's hands when he entered the water. I watched and filmed from below, seeing clearly Neal's tense and strained face peering down into the depths. He snapped it clear of the water with fright when the dolphin swam up towards him. Bill, however, continued to talk to Neal gently and calmly, assuring him he was quite safe. Slowly, very slowly, Neal gained confidence and kept his head submerged for longer and longer periods, watched by the dolphin who stayed around but never swam too close.

Eventually I rose to the surface and asked Bill to let go of Neal's hands. As I was wearing full breathing apparatus all I had to do was to empty my buoyancy regulator to sink slowly back down again. The visibility under water was exceptionally good, and from the sea-bed I could see both walls of the gulley that ran into the dark recesses of a cave, the back of which was in deep shadow. I looked up and saw the dolphin gather speed as he started to circle Neal. Dorad then shot up to the surface and leapt over Neal's back, knifing back into the water to whirl around the cave before once more launching himself into the air for a second jump. I knew Neal would be terrified, and swam up to comfort him. As I surfaced beside him I broke through the air-water interface into a babble of sound just as Dorad crashed back into the sea in a confusion of waves and foam that set Neal rocking and gasping for breath. High above the noise of the splashing came tremendous shouts of applause from those on the *Tuna* with a ringside view of a spectacular dolphin show. Neal, who had absolutely no control whatever over the performing animal, was taking the role of unwilling ringmaster.

Like most of Dorad's performances it was unexpected and over as quickly as it had begun. It took longer for the human enthusiasm to subside. Everyone was shouting congratulations to Neal, who, much to his surprise, had survived the ordeal, to be treated like a returning hero.

Although they had not said so to me, everyone admitted to Neal that they had been genuinely scared the first time they got in the water with the dolphin. He was much bigger than them, and they knew he could kill them in a second if he chose to do so. Among those who confessed to cowardice in the presence of the dolphin was Neal's minder Chris.

Next day we transferred to the largest of all the caves, formed by a massive fissure in the coastline that opened into a pool surrounded by steep walls of rock. It was a powerful place.

We started by cruising in the inflatable outside the cave, between outcrops of rock that ran parallel to the shore. Dorad rode on our bow, under the keel and behind us, constantly switching his position. This made things difficult for the cameraman, who, with one eye sealed to the eyepiece, was expected to respond in a fraction of a second to instructions fired at him whenever the dolphin was spotted. The dolphin leap is short in duration. To get a good film sequence it is necessary to show the scene before, during and after the jump.

'Here he is. He's coming ahead. No he isn't, he's behind us. Moving forward. Now he's disappeared. There he is, over by the *Tuna*. He's coming this way. He's right underneath us . . . coming up front. Over on your right. You've missed him.'

It was when we were in the large cave, however, that the fun really began. Because of the confined space we could see the dolphin virtually all the time, and thought it would be easier there to film the moment *before* he leapt, and then the jump itself, instead of just catching him in mid-flight, which was all we had achieved so far. But try as we might to establish some kind of pattern to his behaviour, we never succeeded. It was as if the dolphin were deliberately trying to confuse us. Sometimes he would rush forward alongside the boat in what we felt sure was the run-up for a spectacular leap. Then at the last minute he would dive down and rocket out of the water behind us while the camera was still running and pointing ahead of the boat. It was expensive in terms of film stock, and not very productive, but it was immensely exciting.

Because of his tendency to seasickness, we had put Neal ashore on a rocky outcrop where he tried to capture the dolphin with his stills camera. The fact that he didn't get the elusive leaping dolphin picture he was hoping for annoyed him. While he was being ferried back to Dingle for the last time, Dorad reared out of the water just in front of the speeding Zodiac and Neal got the shot he wanted. He had succeeded at last, and interpreted that final leap beneath the lighthouse as a gesture of encouragement and farewell on the part of the dolphin.

Bill also had a great send-off, with the dolphin repeatedly thwacking his tail on the water in a succession of the loudest cracks we had heard so far. Bill phoned the O'Connor farm where I was staying as soon as he arrived back in Oxford. Never before in his life had he gambled, but on the ferry back home he had played the fruit machine which coughed out three wins in quick succession. His total take amounted to £115. I could feel him smiling at the other end of the phone. For Bill, coming to Ireland had lived up to all his dreams and expectations.

Reviewing the entire experiment with the film producer the following day, Jon Levy said that of the three patients we had introduced to the dolphin the change in Neal was the most remarkable. At first he didn't think I would succeed at all with Neal, but just before setting off home, he had got the picture he wanted and had swum alone with the dolphin in the big cave.

On our final day, when all of our patients had left, we were joined by Roy Hutchins who had come to Ireland to work with Heathcote Williams on a stage production of *Whale Nation*. I was pleased that Roy was able to experience for himself contact with the dolphin, which was after all a small whale, and hoped that it would enable him to express more fully the feelings evoked by Heathcote's eloquent words.

The pressure was off. The weather was perfect, the sea oily flat, and we had nothing to do but frolic with a dolphin. We rested at anchor, and people jumped overboard to swim with Dorad. I went for a final dive on my own under the rock arch to say a silent farewell to the world of the dolphin. I left all my cameras in the boat and sank into the sea, allowing myself to drift gently through the kelp forest into the jewel-box world of corals, sponges and starfish. Dorad came over a couple of times, looked at me quizzically, detected that I was in a contemplative mood, and then swam away for more vigorous sport with whoever happened to be finning on the surface.

When the last of the snorkellers had returned to the boat and we pulled up the anchor, Dorad became excited, knowing full well what it signified. He shot away from us as we moved off and gave us a stupendous farewell display. He hurtled round the cave like a speed-boat under full power, and performed seven leaps in succession. His playground was in complete shadow and the rock walls were dark grey. His body glistened bright silver and the sound of him crashing back into the sea echoed round the rock chamber and was funnelled out through the cave entrance. It was sheer unrestrained and uninhibited exuberance. To me it was a powerful physical expression of the joyful force that dolphins radiate – a force that is always present, even when they are quiet.

Two hours later my wetsuit had been washed with fresh water for the last time and was hanging up to dry in a barn in the O'Connor farm. In my room I put *The Secret Garden* by David Sun on my portable cassette player and the space around me filled with the sounds of rippling water, bird song and a gently stroked guitar. Sitting cross-legged on the bed, I gazed out through the picture window at the mountains in the far distance, turning lilac and then purple in the slowly fading light. I remained still, mesmerised by the subtle changes that were transforming the sky, the sea and the land.

My body, which earlier in the day had been subjected to the extremes of sun and cold sea, as well as being taken to the limits of physical endurance when I was frolicking with the dolphin, was undergoing a change. The weariness of the day faded until I lost all feeling. Never before had I experienced such serenity and peace of mind. My limbs were slowly invaded by a pleasant numbness that grew and grew until I no longer existed as a person. I became the shadow creeping up the mountainside. I was a beam of yellow light shining through the sea and flickering on the sand. For a time, which had no meaningful dimension in minutes or seconds, I experienced nirvana, that state of bliss in which the individual becomes extinct and is absorbed into some kind of supreme spirit.

· 17 ·

The Dolphin's Touch

It was Southern Television (TVS) which eventually decided to convert the material we had shot in Ireland into a television programme in their series, 'The Human Factor'. The series had a distinct style and format which was not entirely satisfied by our film, and this meant a return to Ireland for some more footage the following year. It was a headache for the producer, Jon Levy, who was looking after the finance. A new director, Garfield Kennedy, reporter Ted Harrison, a film crew and our three patients had to be transported to Ireland for a few days in June. With the limited budget it was a very optimistic plan that relied on the dolphin still being present and co-operative, as well as the notoriously fickle Irish weather being kind to us.

With memories of the previous year still fresh in our minds, the chances of not meeting the dolphin were dismissed. So, despite reports from my contacts that Dorad was still around and very friendly, I felt bound to make it clear to all concerned that we were going out to find a wild dolphin who could be as elusive as a wild goose. For me, if not for the film crew, this element of uncertainty and challenge added spice to the project.

Even so, there was a small nagging worry at the back of my mind that failure to find the dolphin might not be taken lightly by some members of the group. Bill and Neal in particular were expecting great things, and I was anxious to avoid a major setback for them.

As events turned out, we did become the centre of a medical drama but it didn't involve any of my 'patients'. It happened after we had filmed the sequences needed for the television programme and it involved the then future Mayor of Dublin, Ben Briscoe, and his brother Joe. They were staying at the O'Connor farmhouse and became keenly interested in my involvement with dolphins. When they discovered that we had rushes of some of the film on video, they stayed up until well past midnight to watch them.

The older of the two Briscoes, Joe, had seen many dolphins at sea and said they were telepathic. He also claimed that they liked sugar. I had heard the first characteristic ascribed to dolphins many times before, but the second was new to me, and I expressed my scepticism. Joe was insistent, and said he would prove it.

The *Tuna* was already overcrowded when the extra persons turned up on the jetty. Laurence, the skipper, was not willing to welcome any more on to his overloaded boat, and only by stretching the bonds of his friendship with me to the elastic limit were the Briscoe brothers allowed on board with their bags of sugar.

Part of my plan on this return visit was to observe how the dolphin responded to large groups, because that was a situation with which he was being increasingly confronted. The notion that the dolphin could be drawn away from such a group with sugar I thought extremely unlikely. All the same, I could not say to Joe 'I told you so' until we had actually tried the experiment.

The sea was calm as we motored out to the Magic Cave, and on the way I got kitted up so that I could film from sea level with a video camera the party jumping into the water. Owen Davis, a Welshman, had been very helpful throughout the second phase of Operation Sunflower and I wanted to film him entering the sea first, followed quickly by the others. Having positioned myself alongside the *Tuna*, I set the camera running and gave Owen the signal to jump. I had taken no account of either Owen's keenness or his physical prowess. He leapt so high and so far clear of the boat that not so much as a bubble appeared in the part of the sea I was scanning with the camera.

That was failure number one. My plan went to pieces altogether when another boat arrived and an Irishman wearing no more than a pair of swimming trunks immediately jumped into the water. Nature had equipped him with a good layer of insulation with which to resist the Atlantic cold, and he was a very good swimmer. Furthermore, he swam regularly with Dorad who obviously enjoyed playing with him. The dolphin took off for a game and stayed well away from the *Tuna*.

To add to the confusion, one of the fishing boats full of tourists drew up some distance away and what seemed like an entire bus-load of people leapt into the sea. I resigned myself to the prospect of a free-for-all on a grand scale and abandoned any idea of trying to orchestrate events for filming.

Joe Briscoe was totally carried away by his irrepressible desire to get in with the dolphin, regardless of the multitudes already in the sea. He begged the loan of a wetsuit and pulled it on with the speed of a fireman responding to an emergency. So excited was he, and so obsessed with touching the dolphin, that he declined the fins and mask that were offered him. He had no time to put them on. Still zipping up the wetsuit, he flung himself into the ocean and went off at a frenetic pace, swimming for all his might towards the dolphin, who happened at that moment to be near me. By the time Joe reached me, however, the dolphin had moved away towards yet another fishing boat which had come out from the jetty. I recognised one person on board as a visitor from England who had asked me on the jetty if she could come with our group on the *Tuna*.

She had spoken to me before, on the telephone, so I knew that she had problems and was someone who desperately needed to meet Dorad. Unable to take any more passengers on the *Tuna*, I had advised her to go out on one of the fishing boats. From afar I saw her, dressed in a brief swimming costume, launch herself into the sea and swim with confidence towards the dolphin. When Dorad passed near to her, she burst into hysteria and started crying and screaming. Bill, who was in the water and had the attention of the dolphin, immediately swam towards her. Recognising a fellow sufferer, he held her hands and tried to calm her down.

To add to the chaos that now reigned, Joe Briscoe shouted something and swam to the inflatable, which was tied up to the stern of the *Tuna*. Mike Benison hauled the Irishman out of the water and Joe slithered into the Zodiac and remained still. From my position in the sea I couldn't see that he was lying unconscious in the bottom of the Zodiac, but I gathered from Mike's expression that something was wrong.

'Is he okay?' I yelled from some way off.

Mike did not hear me. He bent over Joe and started to unzip his wetsuit. Heathcote, who had detached himself from the other passengers on the *Tuna* and watched the crazy events of the morning from the roof of the cabin, jumped down on to the now almost empty deck. He looked over the stern into the inflatable at Joe who had stopped breathing and whose face was already a sallow grey. In an instant Heathcote had leapt into the Zodiac and put his ear to Joe's chest. Hearing nothing, he started to thump it in an effort to stimulate Joe's heart.

By the time I had swum to the Zodiac Heathcote had been joined by Jeannie Sayre Adams, who was a nurse. She at once recognised that Joe had had a heart attack. Using one of the Zodiac hand-lines, I hauled myself up and looked down into the boat. Jeannie had Joe's head cupped in her arms and was talking in a very soothing voice to him. His heart had started and he was breathing again. His brother Ben was hanging over the stern of the *Tuna* not knowing if his brother would survive. But the crisis was over, and Joe started to recover consciousness.

We knew we had to get the sick man into hospital as soon as possible. Having made sure he had the keys to his car, which was parked on the quay, Ben jumped into the boat where his brother was being nursed by Jeannie, still in her swimming costume, and seconds later was being ferried by Mike at full speed for Dingle. Nobody saw the dolphin again until the inflatable returned later and Mike was able to tell us that by the time he reached the jetty Joe had recovered sufficiently to walk to the car. He was now in hospital, being kept in for observation.

Those on board who were closest to the incident all agreed that without Heathcote's prompt action Joe Briscoe would not have survived to see his younger brother Ben become Mayor of Dublin, just as he predicted he would when first we met. As for his other prediction that Dorad would be attracted to sugar, we never did carry out that experiment.

The number of people involved in the second Operation Sunflower expedition to Dingle was considerably greater than in the first. That was because I wanted to broaden the base of my investigation, and to use the trip to introduce people with different artistic talents to the dolphin. Heathcote Williams, the poet, had already fallen under the dolphin's spell. Among others to do likewise in that summer of 1988 were Larry Conklin, a brilliant new-age guitarist and lyricist, and the glass engraver and artist Emma Wolfenden.

It was also important for Bill, Neal and Jemima to have a reunion with the dolphin. They were more relaxed, now that they knew what to expect. Also the stress of being involved in a film was quickly removed. The weather and the dolphin could not have been more co-operative, so that shooting was completed in two days. All three 'patients' had changed for the better. One of the most marked differences, which would have been apparent even if they had not been depressives, was that *they* were now the dolphin experts and the newcomers were the novices.

There was no doubt in my mind about which of them had outwardly changed the most since the previous year – and that was Neal Jackson. On his second visit he was accompanied by a girlfriend, Sarah, whose presence alone demonstrated a new self-confidence. As well as female company Neal also brought with him a better semi-dry wetsuit, much thicker than the one we had provided. The extra insulation, coupled with a rapid loss of fear of the dolphin, gave Neal a new confidence in the water. On land he displayed fast, jerky and often nervous movements. In the water these were smoothed out. Laurence thought him hardly recognisable as the young man we had brought out with us the previous year. When I watched Neal darting through the water with flashing fins, climbing confidently on to the rocks and then sliding back into the sea to chase after the dolphin, I thought this man has become like a seal. Wild seal or not, his mistrust of humans remained. When he went into the water, I noticed that he put his camera and possessions into his diving bag and secured it with a large padlock, despite the fact that he knew everyone on board.

The person who seemed to have changed least was Bill Bowell. Oblivious to the cold, he just flopped into the sea and would stay there quite happily for hours, clicking his fingers and talking to the dolphin just as he did the first time they met. When he returned to the *Tuna*, his wife Edna was always waiting for him. She must have loved him very dearly to have stayed with him during his decade of darkness when he was totally unresponsive. Now his love for her showed, and he referred to Edna with unbounded affection as his 'Land Dolphin'.

Bill maintained that he knew Edna before she was born. His mother was friend and neighbour to Edna's mother when both were pregnant. Bill was born first, five weeks ahead of Edna, and their names appear on the same page in the Register of Births. The two new mothers were such good friends that they often looked after one another's babies. Bill's mother-in-law had often changed his nappy when his own mother was out at work and he was blowing bubbles at Edna.

Contact was lost when Bill and Edna were still young and the two families moved apart. Then, years later, their two mothers met again, quite by chance. Bill and Edna were both twenty, and for them it was love at second sight. They were married within a year. Bill often expressed the view that he was the luckiest man in the world to have married Edna. None of us who knew his circumstances and had seen the two of them together would have disagreed with that.

Whereas Bill's symptoms were obvious, and the effect of the dolphin upon him was there for all to see, Jemima's case was different because so few people realised she had a problem in the first place. More than one person, seeing our film *The*

Dolphin's Touch on television, has found it hard to believe, Jemima coming across – as she does – as a delightfully intelligent and articulate girl. What they do not see, because we did not film it, is Jemima, when she first arrived in Ireland, huddled in the corner of the Armada Restaurant, not eating and diverting herself with knitting while watching us with the alert but frightened eyes of a cornered fawn.

· 18 ·

Saint Brendan

Sunday was the only day of the week when the locals and visiting Irishmen from as far away as Dublin could go out to see the dolphin. So, leaving Dorad to the Irish, I suggested to Heathcote and his daughter China, who had joined us, that we might visit nearby Mount Brandon together. It was Ireland's second highest peak (3,127 feet) but what interested me was Saint Brendan's, or Brandon's, special relationship with travellers and the sea.

Saint Brendan lived in the fifth century, and tradition has it that he made a voyage in search of the land of eternal youth, discovering America in the process a thousand years before Columbus.

The account, later compiled by monks, of Brendan's seven-year odyssey mentions no identifiable names, but some of the places do bear resemblance to parts of Iceland and the other islands that would lie along a possible sailing route from Ireland to the eastern seaboard of the United States. It captured the interest of scholars of the time and was translated from Irish into English, Latin, Welsh, Scots, Gaelic, French, Saxon and Flemish.

The feasibility of such a journey of discovery was put to a practical test by Tim Severin: in 1977 he set sail from Brandon Creek − by tradition the departure point of the saint − in a vessel made of oxhides stretched over a lattice frame of native Irish ash. After an exciting and eventful voyage lasting 50 days, the *Brendan* (as his vessel was called) reached the New World, demonstrating that Saint Brendan could indeed have

14 The dolphin hung motionless in the water while Bill talked to
him through his snorkel tube

15 The Dingle dolphin responded to many sounds,
including that of the penny whistle

16 The poet Heathcote Williams, who fell for the Dingle dolphin,
gave us juggling lessons

17-18 Above water, the dolphin entertained the visitors to Dingle with his aerial acrobatics; under water, the sun-dappled dolphin would respond to a snorkeller ringing a bell

made such a journey. As Tim Severin had dolphins for company on part of his voyage we can deduce that Saint Brendan was probably familiar with dolphins too.

I had read somewhere that on the last Sunday in June pilgrimages were made to the ruins of an ancient religious settlement on the top of Mount Brandon. It was a revision of an old custom in which penitents climbed the long stony path to the summit on their knees. When they reached the peak, pilgrims would walk round the historic stones uttering prayers. Such was the importance of this ceremony that 20,000 people are said to have taken part in a pilgrimage in 1868 to proclaim their Roman Catholic faith and renounce the Protestant Church.

When I mentioned our intention to watch the procession to Peggy O'Connor, who was a practising Catholic, she said there was no fixed date for the pilgrimage. It happened when it happened, if it happened at all, and was as much dependant on the weather as on the ecclesiastical calendar. She also said that the climb was dangerous when visibility was poor and advised against it. We could take it from her that if we decided to go we would probably be the only ones on the path, and that we could easily get lost.

Abandoning a visit to the place where Saint Brendan was said to have looked out and sighted the land of 'Hy Brasil', I suggested instead a pilgrimage of another kind – to Great Blasket Island. There we would go in search of the spirit of Maurice O'Sullivan. His evocative account of past life on this remote and romantic island in his book *Twenty Years A-Growing* was a piece of classic Irish literature from which both Heathcote and I had derived immense pleasure. On a previous occasion when I had driven from Dingle to Slea Head as the sun was setting, sea and sky ablaze with red, my passenger was so overwhelmed by the sheer beauty of it she cried.

When I took to the same stretch of road again with Heathcote and China as passengers, the sea and the sky were in misty mood. An air of mystery hung over the ancient windowless beehive houses of stone, held together over the centuries by

gravity. Those who built them must have had intuitive understanding of how to construct permanent dwellings for almost
certainly they had no formal knowledge of architecture. We
inspected the Gallarus Oratory, a church constructed by cor-
belling over one thousand years ago and the most perfect
building of its kind. In this technique each stone course is
smaller than the one beneath it, so that the walls eventually
meet to form the roof.

Saint Brendan undoubtedly visited Great Blasket Island,
which has been inhabited for over two thousand years. He
would probably have made the crossing in a curragh, a light
skin-covered rowing boat that skims over the waves. The skins
were later replaced by canvas coated with pitch. They are still
used in regattas today, and we inspected some upturned cur-
raghs, looking like giant legless black beetles, at the foot of a
steep path that led from the road down to the tiny harbour at
Dunquin. The ferry was a small cabin-cruiser with a powerful
engine. Once clear of the harbour, it took only ten minutes to
cross the treacherous strait between the mainland and Great
Blasket Island, which fifty years ago was known as the 'next
parish to America'.

Today it is hard to believe that this island at the mercy of
every eastbound storm that the Atlantic winds hurl at it could
provide in former times a permanent, self-sufficient home for
150 human souls. On a summer's day it is alluring, but one
needs little imagination to realise how difficult it must have
been to sustain life there in winter. Houses were made from
local rock and furniture from driftwood. There was no pub, no
church and no shop.

In the evenings the islanders gathered in one another's houses
to exchange stories passed down orally from one generation
to the next in a language which, in many respects, scholars
thought richer than English. The best storyteller was the most
revered person on the island. The most important visitor was
not the priest, the soldier or the policeman, but the poet who
brought with him old stories from the mainland. Such was the
talent for story-telling in this tiny community that it produced

three world-renowned authors in Maurice O'Sullivan, Tom O'Crohan and Peig Sayers.

In 1953 the government transferred to the mainland what remained of the ageing population. Since then several groups of young idealists have tried to re-establish life on Great Blasket. They were successful during the summer, but their resolve was always broken before the next spring arrived.

From the tiny harbour on Great Blasket we climbed the winding, grassy road – kept closely cropped by sheep – that led past ruined buildings to some houses that were inhabited. One of them was a café, and we tarried there to enjoy some delicious wholesome food served by a young woman whose skirt touched the floor. She had a rare look of inner tranquillity, of security and homeliness that made us feel comfortable and welcome the moment we stepped through the door. While she was attending to our order, the rosy face of a small boy with curly golden hair appeared around the counter. He had blue eyes that sparkled with unconcealed but slightly shy curiosity.

He showed Heathcote his magic lorry. Heathcote then performed some real magic and changed a small two-pence piece into a large copper coin. Heathcote asked the boy if he had a pound note whereupon he disappeared into the kitchen and returned a few moments later triumphantly brandishing one. His look changed to one of horror when, before his very eyes, Heathcote tore the note into tiny pieces and rolled the shreds into a ball which he pushed into his closed fist. A few seconds later the boy's expression changed to incredulous amazement when Heathcote opened his hand and unrolled the ball into a pound note that was wholly intact. The boy called his parents to witness the miracle. Then, producing a two-pence piece from his pocket, he asked the magician if he could change it into a one pound note. When Heathcote obliged, the boy's look of sheer wonder and innocent belief in what had happened was, for Heathcote, more than enough compensation for the two pounds his magic tricks had cost him.

Before we caught the ferry back to Dunquin we walked the length of the island. From the summit we looked down on an archipelago of tiny islands, many surrounded by rings of white foam. We felt the clear air blowing on our faces, watched sheep nibbling the grass and saw seals hauled out on the same long yellow strand from which the young Maurice O'Sullivan had gathered bounty washed ashore from a cargo ship that came to grief on the treacherous rocks beneath Sorrowful Cliff.

When the last permanent inhabitants of Great Blasket were taken off the island, an era came to an end. As the houses fell into disrepair only the memories and the stories remained.

The same wave of progress should also have overwhelmed all other remnants of that bygone age. Fortunately, in Ireland, by some miracle that defies the laws of mass markets and EC economics, a few vestiges survive, though they are perilously close to extinction.

I came across one of them as the result of my work on Operation Sunflower. I received a phone call from a nurse in London who was interested in my theory and almost dropped a bedpan when I told her what I was doing in a sleepy fishing village she would never have heard of called Dingle.

'Sure, wasn't that where I was born,' came her soft Irish lilt down the telephone.

I was invited to visit her parents, and did so at McCarthy's Bar in Dingle. I was given 'hot whiskey', which consists of sugar, hot water, a slice of lemon spiked with cloves and whiskey – Irish, of course. Danny McCarthy told me of the days when farmers would walk their cattle up to 10 miles by road to the market in Dingle. There was a ritual in striking a deal, and when the price was eventually agreed, the money would be counted out in front of a witness. The notes were then rolled and secured with a safety pin in a pocket inside a waistcoat with many buttons – to ensure they got back to the farm, past the bars that lined every road home in Ireland. Not all the money was put in the security pouch however. An agreed sum was given to the witness, who also acted as arbitrator in any dispute, and the remainder provided much needed lubrication for the vocal cords after so much bargaining.

The McCarthy Bar had been in the family for five generations. It was more than just a bar, it was also a shop and a home, all in one small building. The bar and the grocery-cum-confectionery-cum-greengrocery shop were accommodated in one room that opened directly on to the street. In the days when the McCarthy's kept a cow in the back yard, it was not uncommon for the cow to walk through their dining room, across the stone-flagged floor in the bar/shop and out into the street. Even now it was necessary for the customers to pass through the living room, where I was sitting, to get to the lavatory at the back.

I was told that there used to be a snug, which was removed when the place was modernised – much to the regret of John Mills who frequented McCarthy's during the filming of *Ryan's Daughter* in the late 1960s. The arrival of stars such as Robert Mitchum, and a huge film crew, brought undreamt of riches to the impoverished town of Dingle. Mere mention of the film was enough to send Danny's wife Ita into reveries about the halcyon days when money flowed like never before. People were attracted from far and wide, among them Mark Kerry, the proprietor of the Armada restaurant, who came from Dublin to help feed the film crew and liked Dingle so much that he decided to stay. All that *Ryan's Daughter* seemed to have in common with our film was the two years it took to make. I doubt if our entire budget would have hired Mitchum for more than a couple of days.

McCarthy's Bar was next door to a school, and so also served as the school tuck shop, dispensing wine gums to the children and Guinness to the teachers in the same room – or was it the other way round? Such was the McCarthy hospitality, I wasn't sure when I left.

Although their bar was a reminder of a bygone era, the McCarthys themselves had moved with the times. They cherished their memories of the past but enjoyed the benefits, such as travel and exotic foods, that came with the new age of prosperity. Paddy Ferriter in the lighthouse, on the other hand, ate simply and elected deliberately to go no further afield than the beach.

His lifestyle was probably closer to that of the original Blasket Islanders than anyone living in Ireland. Yet even he was unable to hold out against the television invasion. When our film about Dorad the dolphin was finally finished, and transmitted in the United Kingdom on 18 September 1988, the programme could be picked up in Dublin but not on the west coast. The director, Garfield Kennedy, took with him on holiday in Dingle a video player and a VHS copy of the programme. On the day of transmission he humped the gear across the fields and set it up in the lighthouse so that he and Paddy could see it together on the same day that *The Dolphin's Touch* was watched by millions in the United Kingdom. For Paddy it was as magical and incredible to see himself talking about the dolphin to Bill Bowell as it was for the boy on Great Blasket Island to watch Heathcote, the alchemist, transmute a two-pence piece into a pound note.

Paddy will probably be dead when the boy grows up and realises that it is not possible to turn two pence into a pound. When Paddy passes on, we will have moved still further into an era in which those who operate computers and stare at VDUs, not poets, are the most important members of society. But in the new age of teeming technology and information pollution will dolphins, mystics and magicians have anything of real value to contribute to civilisation? After a visit to Australia I felt sure they would.

· 19 ·

Oceania, an Australian Dream

On 24 November 1976 *The Times* newspaper carried a report by Ross Warneke on what he described as 'one of the most eccentric scientific experiments of the century'. He described a spaceship, still at the drawing-board stage, designed not to travel through the vast barren emptiness of outer space to Mars or Venus but to explore the inner space of our own planet, the oceans, where it was hoped two-way communications would be set up with the intelligent inhabitants of that space – the dolphins. Hence the name of the craft – *Dolphin Embassy*.

The *Dolphin Embassy* was the brainchild of two young Americans, Doug Michels, an architect and artist, and Doug Hutt, an oceanographer and boat builder. The idea first came to them in 1973 when the exploitation of whales and dolphins was receiving considerable media coverage. In their minds they searched for methods of bringing together the adversaries in this deadly one-sided war. Their fantasy took the form of a craft that could submerge and be piloted by man or dolphin. It would employ 1990s computer technology to enable the two intelligences to communicate with one another. They drew up rough sketches of the inner spaceship, but their ideas did not move forward until they visited Australia two years later. There, off Townsville and Mackay, they saw an enormous number of whales and dolphins. In Arnhem Land they learnt that the Australian Aborigines once talked and worked with dolphins.

These discoveries provided just the encouragement they needed to advance their ideas to the next stage. When they returned to the United States, plans were drawn up by the Ant Farm design agency in a cargo shed in San Francisco's dockland for a ferro-concrete boat which *The Times* reporter said was 'more bizarre than anything built by Hollywood's science fiction film producers'. The design included advanced audio and video equipment, with feedback capabilities which would enable the crew of scientists and artists to scrutinise their own interaction with the dolphins. The idea was to involve an architectural group at Sydney Institute of Technology in the construction of the *Dolphin Embassy*, which would then be launched in the waters off The Great Barrier Reef where there was a large dolphin population. Grants were obtained, and a report was issued in Australia in 1978 announcing plans to build a vessel which would be self-sufficient and include equipment for desalination, solar heating and hydroponic food growing. It also stated that the crew would consist of twelve scientists, and that non-scientists and children would also be included, the latter on the grounds that 'the naive observations of children will be treated with credibility equal to complex computer theory.'

The *Dolphin Embassy* never got beyond a design, and a dream. It did, however, capture many people's imaginations. Only time will tell if, like many other visions dismissed as absurd or too fanciful when first proclaimed, it will ever become a reality.

One of the young architects involved in the project in Australia was Bob Perry, and I was to see for myself just how greatly influenced he was by the concept. Shortly after touching down at Sydney Airport in May 1988, I was whisked away to the Darling Harbour complex for a television interview beneath a magnificent sculpture of humans and dolphins rising in a spiral above Mother Earth. This beautiful modern sculpture in stainless steel was backed by a fountain. The entire showpiece, together with shops, cafés and promenades, was enclosed in an enormous curved canopy filled with glistening glass panels and appropriately called the Crystal Galleria.

The architect in charge of this pleasing new development,

then in the final stages of construction, was Bob Perry who, unable to visit the dolphins in their world, had so brilliantly brought their images into a capsule where humans gathered in a bright festive atmosphere to eat and spend their leisure hours. He had not just used dolphin statues to beautify his magnificent edifice; he had included dolphin ethos as well.

The transformation of Sydney's Darling Harbour from a derelict dock area into a striking leisure and business complex serviced by a new monorail was part of the celebrations for the bicentenary of New South Wales. The dolphin was a joyful representation of how Bob Perry saw the future of Australia developing over the next hundred years. Its overall philosophy he called Oceania.

Oceania embodied a dream for the future, in which space-age technology would eliminate outmoded concepts, such as the degrading drudgery associated with many methods of industrial production. We would be launched into a world where, like dolphins in the sea, we would be more caring for one another. Creating more beautiful spaces, especially in urban areas, would be a step towards everyone living in more harmonious surroundings.

I later met Bob Perry beside the dolphin fountain and learnt that the Crystal Galleria, and the Oceania mode of thinking that went with it, was much admired in other parts of the world. So much so that he had been asked to carry forward the concept in other countries.

I had visited Australia on previous occasions, but in 1988 the atmosphere was tangibly different. It seemed to me that quite suddenly Australia had grown up as a nation and become more sophisticated. What was much more exciting, however, was the impression I gained that a new age, a dolphin age if you like, was being born.

There was no more determined a protagonist and promoter of the Oceania idea than Estelle Myers. She met my wife and me at the airport, opened her home in Sydney to us, arranged a host of media interviews for me and whisked us from one event to the next around Australia in her little car. I had known

Estelle for several years and thought of her as the most dynamic person I had ever met. She called herself Motormouth because she never stopped talking. She was impetuous, needed little sleep, tackled everything she did as if she were rocket-propelled, and was also extremely effective. Her coruscating intelligence and forthright expression of her views on the way women were often treated in a male-dominated society unnerved many men, especially those in positions of power in dogma-ridden institutions. Women striving less forcefully to make headway sometimes felt uneasy about the speed with which she worked to remove the injustices of Western society as she saw them.

Estelle was a latter-day suffragette who wanted the world to be filled with love, freedom and equality. She did not endear herself to everyone, especially those who found themselves at odds with the radical changes she was trying to bring about in the attitude and practice of human childbirth. The bee that buzzed around most noisily in Estelle's bonnet was underwater birthing.

The person whose work inspired her most was the Russian pioneer of underwater delivery, Igor Tjarkovsky, who had devoted more than thirty years of his life to research and practice in this field. As a Russian he was brought up in a culture halfway between East and West, in which the boundaries of science and art are more loosely defined.

In his early life near the Siberian-Mongolian border Igor Tjarkovsky came into contact with traditional 'healers', people who use their energy to influence and heal others. Later he took a technical degree, worked as a boat builder, changed to becoming an athletic coach and then qualified as a male midwife. This extraordinary combination of interests and learning sparked in Tjarkovsky the idea that the passage of a newborn baby from the warm, weightlessness of the amniotic fluid in the womb into the noisy, harsh, gravity-laden world of air would be far less stressful to the mother and the child if it took place gently through water. His ideas extended when he saved the life of his premature daughter, Veta, by caring for her in a tub of luke-warm water. She developed surprisingly rapidly and soon caught up with her peers. Veta became the first of a new generation of genuine Water Babies, whose contact with water was maintained from the moment of childbirth.

In 1985 Estelle visited Moscow and filmed Tjarkovsky attending a birth in a bathtub. She flew from Russia to England and swept into our house like a tornado, anxious to show me on video what she had achieved in her whirlwind visit. In an unbroken stream of sentences, fired at machine-gun speed, she untangled the grapevine of cables hanging down behind the television set, connected her own equipment into our system and was proudly running the film she had taken just a few days before in Moscow. In addition to showing babies being born under water she also showed infants at later stages in life as strong, but above all peaceful and calm individuals. The climax came when we watched a large group of them gather in the snow in Gorky Park, where many of them dunked themselves in the ice-cold water of the lake.

Tjarkovsky was not the only person to pursue the concept of giving birth under water. The best-known pioneer of the method in Western Europe was the French physician Michel Odent, with whom Estelle had also made contact, though not on this flying visit.

For Tjarkovsky, underwater birthing is part of an aquatic lifestyle which commences before birth, with the expectant mother spending a great deal of time in the water, often in the presence of the child's father and other parents who are water training their babies under his supervision. The baby is then delivered into the weightless and familiar world of water from which it has just come, and is very carefully looked after while it remains submerged. After a time the mother lifts it out gently and unhurriedly to meet the force of gravity. Thereafter the baby is frequently returned to the water, and will even breastfeed when submerged, with the mother sensing the moment to lift her baby's face clear of the water to take a breath of air.

Some midwives, trained with strict codes of conduct for delivery and post-natal care, find Tjarkovsky's methods totally unacceptable. Yet he has faced opposition from the start, and claims that his results speak for themselves. When he was first allowed out of Russia in 1989, he thrilled and outraged British audiences with his highly controversial theories and practices involving water in birth and child development. As a midwife Tjarkovsky places strong emphasis on establishing close bonds between the baby and its parents before, during and after parturition, with water acting as a conductor between them.

Tjarkovsky, the visionary, has believed for a long time that dolphins have a powerful biofield which could be beneficial to everyone, especially babies, enhancing their sense of security. In 1979 he was able to put his theory to the test when he took a group of female athletes, pregnant mothers and children ranging in age from eight days to eight years on an expedition to a dolphin research station by the Black Sea. The results of this study, summarised in Erik Sidenbladh's book, *Water Babies*, revealed that very young children have a profound natural affinity with dolphins, and vice versa.

I had gone to Australia to attend the First International Whale and Dolphin Conference organised by Kamala Hope-Campbell. Estelle gave a presentation at the conference and spoke of a new species on earth, *Homo delphinus* – babies born in the sea in the presence of dolphins. Strong, healthy and loving, they would grow up without displaying the greed and aggression that cause so much pain and sorrow in us *Homo sapiens*. And this is precisely what Igor Tjarkovsky had been doing – believe it or not, delivering babies in the sea in the presence of dolphins!

I admitted to her that, although I found the idea interesting, I was sceptical. I knew little about underwater birthing, but she was flying in the face of the Darwinian theory of evolution upon which my scientific training was based. Furthermore, what she was saying smacked of the theories of another Russian, now totally discredited, who maintained that if you cut off the tails of dogs often enough they would produce puppies with no tails at all. In my book, once an egg was fertilised, the gene pattern was fixed, and could not be changed by exposing it to dolphin influence, which neither Tjarkovsky nor I could measure anyway.

At the conference I also met Dr Betsy Smith who had to battle with even greater problems than me when it came to applying science to her dolphin studies. To my knowledge, she was the only qualified medical scientist in the world (apart from myself) investigating the effect dolphins might have on humans with clinically diagnosed mental problems, and had published some details of her work. She was looking into the possibility that dolphins might help young people suffering from autism, a condition in which, as a result of neurological impairment, those afflicted isolate themselves mentally and do not communicate or interact socially. As an Associate Professor at Florida International University Dr Smith was obliged to construct her experiments in such a way that they would satisfy established medical scientific procedures. She therefore attempted to compare the behaviour of a small group of autistic children who were brought into contact with dolphins with others (called a control group) who just played on the beach. The data she collected were subjected to standard methods of statistical analysis and showed no detectable difference between the two groups. In the eyes of the scientific world, Dr Smith's case was unproven. Although negative results are useful, most would regard her experiments as a failure. There were others, however, who *knew* that Dr Smith's work should not be interpreted in this way. These were the parents of the young-sters involved. Certainly none of these children were cured, yet the parents all saw noticeable improvements in the behaviour of their offspring *after* they had been with the dolphins.

Dr John Lilly, probably the most famous and controversial dolphin researcher in the world, presented a video of his work with captive dolphins years before but only sparked into life with flashes of wit and genius when the audience questioned him on whether he thought dolphins were extra-terrestrials, as some clearly believed. Coming to grips with John Lilly was like trying to pick up a handful of mercury – one minute you think you've got it, the next it has disappeared through your fingers. I failed miserably when I tried to interview him formally, as a fellow researcher, for a video film we were making. Bill Rossiter of the Cetacean Society International adopted a more aggressive approach. As a result the dolphin guru tossed a pearl to his audience.

'What is so special about looking into the eye of a whale?' Bill asked.

'You are zapped,' was the laconic reply.

'What do you mean by that?' asked Rossiter.

'What do you think it means?' said John Lilly, taking the easy way out.

'That's not good enough, John,' Bill snapped back angrily. 'I asked you what you meant by zapped.'

Lilly went on to explain 'zapped' with an analogy. When a weather satellite circles the earth it 'zaps' back the information it has gathered over a period of time and during several orbits. Nobody on the ground can take in all the data at that one small instant of transmission. The information-packed signal has to be fed into a computer which then prints the message on to charts which can be understood and interpreted by meteorologists. That process takes time and happens after the event. Likewise, when you look into the eye of a whale you are 'zapped'. Not until the event is over, and you unravel the message, can you begin to understand what it conveys.

When asked what the message from the whales was, Lilly replied, 'Blah, blah, blah!' and walked away smiling.

The implication to those listening was that it was not possible to explain the message scientifically. Yet some of the mystics in the audience, who had looked into the eye of a whale, knew that for them it was an intensely emotional and fulfilling experience which they accepted without question and for which a logical explanation was quite unnecessary.

Although for many of the delegates the 'attunement' before the conference sessions began came as no surprise, for me it was. Before the first paper was delivered, Chris James, who looked like a young Yul Brynner, got the audience and the speakers to shake themselves. He then started everyone chanting, and conducted them as he would a choir, directing different sections to hum various notes and then harmonising them. The idea was to relieve stress and inhibitions in both the audience and the presenters. And it worked. On the third and final day the delegates gathered on the beach for this ritual, which was being filmed by Keith Watson with a video camera for a film Estelle and I were making. I was acting as sound recordist and was wearing earphones. It was a marvellous experience for me because I was able to turn up the volume and fill my head with sound. When the singing faded, I swung the microphone round to pick up the roaring of the surf crashing on to the beach behind us, and beyond which the dolphins were on patrol.

An interview between Tarananth Andre and me was also filmed. I had made contact with Tarananth just two years previously when she first became interested in dolphins. She had studied Aborigine culture and knew that some Aborigines had dolphins as their totems, and that this gave them a very special knowledge of dolphins. In collaboration with a young musician, Glenda Lum, she had explored mixing dolphin sounds with musical improvisations. They discovered that amazing transformations took place when this music, plus whale and dolphin sounds, were combined with relaxation and controlled breathing. They called the state of induced euphoria *Dolphin Dreamtime*, and produced a tape cassette.

Playing the tape had a very powerful effect upon me when I was at Valla Beach, but it was when listening to it later in Melbourne that I had an experience which was new and totally unexpected. It happened shortly before my return to England while my wife and I were staying with Cookie Harkin and her family. Cookie ran *Babyswim* – a programme which got babies swimming at a very early age. Lessons took place in warm, saline water in a swimming pool at her home. I had seen some of the results of her work when I swam in the pool with a host of her mothers whose babies swam as happily under water as they did on the surface.

I also spent time floating in the pool with John Lilly who was visiting Melbourne, like me, to take part in a dolphin workshop. By the last night of my stay I have to admit I was physically tired and mentally exhausted with all the new concepts and ideas I had tried to assimilate since my arrival in Australia. So it was with great relief that I escaped to the warm and comforting pool. I loaded the *Dolphin Dreamtime* cassette into a tape player.

With a small float under my neck, and another behind my knees, I lay supine on the water letting the music carry me away. It was dark, nobody else was around, and I was isolated, mentally drifting in an ocean filled with whale and dolphin sounds, interspersed with strange melodies and improvised Westernised versions of Aborigine didgeridoo music. I was talked into this world on the tape by Tarananth counting me down flights of steps into caves full of crystals and beautiful plants and animals. Finally I reached the sea where the dolphins, clearly bathed in sunshine in my mind, were waiting for me.

My eyes closed. I had no idea where I was in relation to the edge of the pool. I touched the side of the pool and gently pushed myself away with my arm. As I did so I felt the water flowing over my body. But it did not stop when I stopped moving for I was no longer Horace Dobbs. I was a dolphin filled with joy, gliding through a sun-filled sea, and enjoying the sensation of water streaming over my body. After a few moments I changed without warning into an eagle wheeling high above dark mountain peaks. With arms outstretched I waggled my fingers to alter the feathers at the tips of my wings to control my flight and trace immense invisible spirals in the sky. All the pressures of the interviews and lectures had gone. There was no one wanting my attention. I was free, I was alone, I was an eagle swooping and climbing through the clean, cool, clear mountain air. Then through the music which had carried me aloft I heard Tarananth's voice and I became a dolphin. As she talked me back through the cave and up the steps, I took a human form and became myself again. Physically I have no doubt that my body stayed floating on Cookie's pool, but the essential me, which had neither weight nor length, had left my body and taken on the form of a dolphin and an eagle.

I had evidence on films and in photographs of many of the remarkable events that had happened when I had been with dolphins. But I could never prove to anyone that I knew what it was like actually to be a dolphin. To me this was disturbing. I knew that if anyone else had told me they had become a dolphin or an eagle I would have been more than sceptical, and I considered myself fairly open-minded. To a person with old-fashioned rigid views, like my mother, who still does not believe humans have landed on the moon because she does not trust what she sees on television and thinks we do not have a right to be on the moon anyway, the mere notion of a white man having an out-of-body experience stemming from a black Aboriginal dreamtime would be beyond belief. To hint that it had happened to me would cause her great concern about the state of mind of her eldest son. Many others, more worldly wise, but less charitable than my mother would undoubtedly consider me quite mad. Yet it was all intensely real, and I had no doubt in my mind that between them Tarananth Andre and Glenda Lum had managed to capture and express something of the spirit of the dolphin.

Although I decided to say little about my experience until I had tested the effect of the tape on other people, I was excited by the prospect that, somehow or other, I might be able to apply my discovery to Operation Sunflower. I asked myself, could *Dolphin Dreamtime* really help people suffering from depression?

The question produced no answer immediately, but it set off a chain of thought from which a clear way forward emerged for Operation Sunflower. The moment of inspiration, if you can call it that, came as a result of bringing together memories and images of three surprisingly different events in different places at different times. One was the experience I had when listening to the *Dolphin Dreamtime* music while afloat in Cookie Harkin's pool; another was something Bill said after he had his first swim with the dolphin in Dingle; and the third, and perhaps most crucial, was a metaphorical meeting with Marilyn Monroe in France in 1987.

· 20 ·

Marilyn Monroe and Tchaikovsky

One aspect of Operation Sunflower haunted me: what would I do if the project proved really successful? Already more people in Britain were being treated for mental illness than any other single medical condition. An American psychotherapist told me that as the pressure of society built up and life became faster we could expect one person in twelve to need some form of mental therapy during his or her lifetime. The prospect was both horrifying and daunting. With the population of Britain at around sixty million, that meant five million in Britain alone would be looking for help. Even if his forecasts were wrong, and only a small percentage of those afflicted felt drawn towards dolphins, the numbers involved were far more than I and the handful of friendly dolphins around the world could ever hope to cope with.

This would put me in the position of dangling a carrot of hope in front of countless people and adding to their anguish by denying all but a small number of them the chance of realising the dream of escaping from the black holes in which they were trapped. Knowing the lengths to which sick people were prepared to go to find cures, I conjured up images that would have been amusing if they were not so frightening or tragic. Imagine the cliffs beneath Dingle lighthouse becoming crowded with depressives like the sacred spots on the Ganges where Hindus gather in their thousands to cleanse themselves spiritually in the holy waters.

My dilemma was compounded by what Bill Bowell had said after his first meeting with the dolphin in Dingle.

'Horace,' he said, 'wouldn't it be wonderful if we could bottle dolphins and put them in every psychiatric ward in the country.'

I knew he was speaking metaphorically – but I understood exactly what he meant. He was thinking about all the other people he knew back at the Warneford Hospital in Oxford who would never be able to experience firsthand the release from the black pit of depression as he had.

When he made this remark there was too much going on all around for me to do more than file his comment away in my brain. Scientists have no idea how such sentences are locked away in our subconscious minds, waiting to be retrieved by any one of a host of stimuli that can trigger the memory. So I registered the comment. Some time afterwards, by an even more mysterious process, I linked Bill's words in Ireland with a bunch of memories labelled *Marilyn Monroe* which were also stored in the amazing labyrinths of my memory bank.

My memories of Marilyn Monroe go back a long way – to the time when I enjoyed her films and heard about her tragic death in 1962. There is, however, a recent entry. It is one of those images I can pull back into my conscious mind and relive with almost the clarity of the day itself. When I do so I am in France in 1987, on a cycling holiday with my wife. I prop up my bicycle by winding the pedal backwards on to the kerb and leave it standing there in order to study a book-shop's window display. The centre of the window has a poster bearing an unmistakable image – a larger-than-life portrait of Marilyn Monroe. Around it are arranged a whole assortment of books about her. I wander into the shop and thumb through them. I discover that she was born in 1926 and realise, to my surprise, that if she were alive at this moment she would be 64, an age by which many women have become grandmothers, or even great-grandmothers. Yet the charismatic beauty of Marilyn Monroe's youth is eternal. Indeed, knowing how many of my contemporaries and young associates are bewitched by her, I realise that her hypnotic beauty has spanned a generation and is even more alive today than it was before she died.

Linking the memory of Bill's comment with the realisation that Marilyn Monroe's allure has not diminished, but has if anything increased over the years, made me wonder if we could package dolphins, or 'bottle dolphins' as Bill put it, in a similar way. Like millions of others, I had fallen under her spell, yet I had never met her. So could the millions who had never met Dorad or Simo fall under their spells too?

Memories of another glamorous film star, and an analogy with music, caused me to be mildly optimistic: Ingrid Bergman had Humphrey Bogart under her spell in the film *Casablanca*. In one of the most memorable scenes, set late one night in the Café Americain, Rick (Bogart), who has been drinking to drown his sorrows, asks Sam, the black musician upon whom he is unloading his troubles, to play 'As Time Goes By'. When the pianist begins to play Bogart wallows in the anguish of his separation from the woman he loves. He deliberately uses the music to manipulate his emotions.

Music can change our moods. Indeed, this is precisely what some composers set out to do. Peter Ilich Tchaikovsky demonstrated his particular genius at so doing when he composed his Symphony No. 6 – the *'Pathétique'*. In this classical masterpiece there are stirring passages that make us feel triumphant. In the *Adagio lamentoso* at the end of the work however, the music evokes feelings of such melancholy that some listeners are moved to tears when they hear it.

The mental mechanisms by which music and other forms of art can alter our states of mind is a subject that has puzzled me for a long time. We know which parts of the brain receive the primary input from our ears and our eyes, and it is generally accepted that it is the subsequent transmission of signals into the so-called 'silent' parts of the brain, the cerebral cortex, that are responsible for the feeling of well-being we experience when we enjoy listening to a piece of music. However a familiarisation process is necessary before this can take place. To comprehend this I envisage the brain as a computer and our intellect, intelligence and aesthetic experience as different computer programmes which need to be built up, tested, and then reinforced before they function properly. Thus, from the moment we are born, sound signals come into the brain, and when some of them gather together in a harmonious mode, weak neuronal connections are made which eventually break down if they are not renewed occasionally. Like adding fibres to a strand of rope our appreciation of musical sounds is gradually strengthened. So our enjoyment of music comes with musical education in the broadest sense, and with musical experience. It is a continual process, but we need to reach a critical brain mass before attaining higher levels of aesthetic appreciation, not normally possible when we are very young children. Most children of five cannot fully appreciate Mozart or Haydn. Full enjoyment of classical music does not usually come until we reach adulthood. But the primary connections are made in the early years when our brains are growing in size. Sayings like, 'Give me the child and I will give you the man', and 'You can't teach an old dog new tricks', indicate the importance of our formative years and the slowing down of the process as we get older.

The necessity for this time-consuming learning process is illustrated by the response Tchaikovsky received when he conducted the first performance of his *Pathétique* symphony in 1893. He was given a five minute ovation when he first appeared on the rostrum, but as the performance progressed, the audience became restive and eventually booed. This was not because they were unsympathetic, or unintelligent. It was due to their being *unfamiliar* with what later became recognised as one of the composer's greatest masterpieces.

One of the few things that Marilyn Monroe and Tchaikovsky have in common is that they are both no longer with us in body, but their magic lives on because we have technology. In other words, we have 'bottled' them.

With audio and video tapes we can recreate their magic at will in our homes, or in psychiatric wards, but we can do more than that. We can refine the image during the bottling process to improve it and amplify it. We can edit out the bad bits and emphasise the good. We can change a flat sound into a round sound. We can print pictures of Marilyn Monroe's face ten times larger than life. We can touch out the warts if there are any, add sparkle to the eyes, and airbrush out ageing lines. In blatantly commercial and marketing terms, we can manipulate the product to satisfy the needs and wishes of the consumer.

It was the realisation of these possibilities that led me to the idea that we should attempt to produce dolphin images specially for people suffering from depression. In November 1988, in a brief progress report on Operation Sunflower for International Dolphin Watch, I proposed the production of what I termed *audio pills* and *video pills*.

We already had material to provide starting points for both of these concepts: the *Dolphin Dreamtime* tape for our audio pill and video copies of my films *Bewitched by a Dolphin* and *The Dolphin's Touch* for visual pills. Having clearly identified a way forward, I embarked on the next stage of Operation Sunflower, which I knew would be a long-term phase of the project. I did so with my usual optimism, knowing that it needed to evolve as it progressed, with input coming from sources which had yet to make themselves known to me, but which would arise, quite spontaneously at the right moment, just as they always had done in the past.

It would take many years to open people's minds to the idea that dolphins may be able to help them, just as it had taken time for us to understand the paintings of van Gogh and to fully appreciate the music of Tchaikovsky. I therefore had also to include educational and familiarisation elements in the long-term programme before enough evidence would be available to convince the sceptics of the validity of my theory – and it still was only a theory – that images of dolphins could change the state of the human mind and help depressives. Yet there might be one way of leap-frogging this time-lag. It was to pose my theory and observe the effect on a group that I knew was already receptive to the principles behind it. I decided therefore to put my 'bottled dolphins' to the test at the College of Psychic Studies in London, where I had agreed to conduct a workshop entitled 'The Healing Potential of Dolphins' in March 1989.

I had never liked the word 'workshop' because somehow, for me, it conjures up visions of the workhouse and sweated labour on production lines. When I commenced my presentation I told the audience that I was going to run a 'playshop', in keeping with my dolphin philosophy – that most of us take life far too seriously and should put an element of fun into everything we do, even when considering serious issues, such as depression.

After explaining what joy I had seen dolphins bring into my own and other people's lives, and illustrating this with my films, I concluded my playshop by asking everyone to listen to one side of the *Dolphin Dreamtime* tape, which lasted for thirty minutes.

I did not allow the music to carry me away but instead watched the members of the audience who, with just a few exceptions, appeared to go into a trance-like state.

Typical of the letters I received afterwards was one from Monica Larkin, asking for a tape to play to a friend who was terminally ill. Here is what she wrote afterwards:

When I listened to it (the *Dolphin Dreamtime* tape) first, at the end of your London seminar, I was amazed! I've prac- tised various forms of relaxation but have never felt as good as during the Australian tape. I really felt as if I *was* a dolphin and talking back to those on the tape. Then my hands and arms rose up from my lap!! As the music finished they went back down. I really felt I could float off the chair. I regard my self as quite a grounded down to earth bod – so, as you can imagine, I was surprised by the effect of the tape.

I've played it to Rita Tarr – the friend who is in the Royal Marsden Hospital. She is very ill, and apart from a break of 11 days at home, has been there since 29 November 1988. I'm going to play it again with her over the weekend. She's almost too poorly to switch on the player herself. When she's experienced it a few times I'll write to you again and give her reactions.

Monica's response was exactly the kind of spontaneous reaction I was hoping for. I had emphasised to the audience that I was definitely not setting out to make *claims*. All I wanted was to make *observations* and leave anyone who was interested to draw their own conclusions.

I knew my *modus operandi* would not satisfy those who were looking for proof that I was on the right lines. Yet I was in the wonderful position of not being answerable to a committee or a board of directors. I had only to satisfy myself. I therefore did what I *felt* was right. I was not prepared to box in my field of observation with fences defined by statisticians.

I had no idea what the outcome of Monica Larkin's experiment would be. But when I sent her one of the *Dolphin Dreamtime* tapes I *knew* that Operation Sunflower was moving in the right direction.

In 1987 I visited my medical mentor who had guided me when I first started organising clinical trials in hospitals over two decades earlier. The old man, now sadly dead, was from the old school. Any new idea needed to be supported by irrefutable hard clinical data before it became acceptable to him. We became very fond of one another despite the sparks that often flew when we discussed controversial issues. Although he was very sick the last time I saw him he listened to my ideas on Operation Sunflower with his usual patience. He offered to help, and then put forward his suggestions on how he thought I should proceed. Unfortunately they would have taken me in almost exactly the opposite direction to the one I had chosen to pursue after so much heart-searching. Before I left he said, in his usual forthright and uninhibited manner, 'Horace, I can't really go along with this comparison with Vincent van Gogh. He was not a proper artist. Now if you were talking about Constable – then I could understand you. John Constable was a *real* painter.'

Fortunately I was able to balance this remark in my mind with the sentiments expressed in the letter I received from Rosie

Dewitt who had attended one of my film shows in Belfast after what for her had been an exceptionally harrowing day.

It was as if I had come into the hall with a mental radio playing out about six stations at once inside my head which the film and talk helped to overcome. But suddenly I had a picture of a dolphin in my mind and at once I had the feeling that I was in some sort of contact with a dolphin.

When all this happened I felt a blissful peace and all the mental ding dong was exchanged for serenity. I felt an emotion which I find very hard to describe to you.

After a few moments of being almost stunned by this extraordinary experience the critical part of my mind began to throw in ideas such as . . . 'a good experience, yes, but not really connected with a dolphin!'

Then I experienced a sort of mental battle with this idea continually coming for a few minutes and each time it arose in my mind the idea that this was a dolphin communication gently overpowered it until it arose no more.

We can tell people about experiences we have, but not so easily the depth or power and beauty of them. But that is one extraordinary one I won't forget.

· 21 ·

Living with a Black Dog

Before giving my presentation at the College of Psychic Studies I felt it was time to take stock; to collect together my thoughts and observations and see if they made sense. Only then could I draw any conclusions.

I started with depression in general. Many forms of depression have been attributed to the ever increasing pace of life and the pressure-cooker society in which most of us now are forced to live. Manic depression, however, is not a condition specific to modern times. It has been a feature of many of the people who have changed the course of human destiny over the centuries. Their number includes generals, artists, politicians, musicians and even scientists. During the high points of their lives they would be intensely creative and strive with tremendous vigour to achieve their goals. But in the troughs that followed they were plunged into self-doubt, disillusionment, dissatisfaction and despair. Some, like Winston Churchill, recognise their condition; he referred to his fits of depression as his 'black dog' and learned to live with them. For others, less able to cope with bouts of the blues, the consequences were disastrous, many attempting, and some succeeding, in committing suicide.

Manic depression has been likened to an emotional roller coaster with bad brakes. In view of the generation spans it covers, it is almost certainly a personality trait that is carried genetically and can be present to a greater or lesser degree in those who suffer from it. In some instances manic depression has been found to be related to a lithium imbalance and chemotherapy has effectively filled in the depressions. However, finding the optimum level of medication is a balancing act that needs careful adjustment because treatment may also cut the highs in life. One author who was given lithium treatment found he no longer had lows but had no highs either, and completely lost the creative urge to write.

Some psychiatrists claim that 1 per cent of human society is manic depressive, and Tricia Kirkman fell into that group. Her life was like the Alps, with soaring peaks and deep black ravines. She once said to me, 'Horace, sometimes I feel so intensely happy, I feel I could burst with joy. Then, just as if a switch is flicked, often for no apparent reason, I plunge into a state of terrible anxiety.'

Although I could not account for such sudden dramatic changes in her feelings I could understand the wide range of passion she felt. This I attributed to her exceptional sensitivity, which manifested itself when she first met Percy. She was immediately able to detect and experience the force that emanated from the dolphin. She became enraptured by him at their very first meeting despite the intense fear she experienced at the same time.

So I asked myself, did meeting the dolphin really do anything for her? And if so, had her life been changed for the better since?

My answer to the first question was 'Yes,' but Percy had not changed Tricia's personality. Seven years after the event she was still likely to break into tears of joy at seeing a beautiful flower or burst into a violent rage at an injustice, or the sight of anyone mistreating a child or an animal. Meeting Percy and Simo and making a film had opened doors that previously had been tightly shut to her. She discovered corridors beyond them where everything was not starkly black or white. With these discoveries she was able to bring her life more under control. For a person with her traumatic past that was a very positive step forward. So that clearly answered the second question. Also I think her love affair with Simo helped to fill the emotional gap in her life between childhood and parenthood.

Tricia's sensitivity and experiences in life made her an ideal counsellor for the three clinical depressives recruited to take part in the first stage of Operation Sunflower. She could relate to all of them because she knew, to some extent at least, what each of them was going through.

When I first met Tricia she was painfully thin, and although she would not consciously admit it, she lived in a permanent state of hunger. Now humans are hunters as well as gatherers. When hunting animals are hungry their senses are heightened. With their appetites satisfied, the majority of them – lions, for example – are content to sit down and sleep, or simply laze the day away. Thus Tricia's undernourished state made her even more sensitive and susceptible to her own feelings. She had an abhorrence of gross obesity and a terrible fear of getting fat. She could sympathise with Jemima Biggs, whose life was dominated by her eating habits. Tricia also knew what it was like to be in what Bill Bowell described as his 'black hole', and she certainly understood the dreadful feeling of being unable to cope that plagued Neal Jackson. Tricia also spoke to Neal's mother because she was a parent herself and knew the strain that his condition was imposing upon both his mother and father.

Let us now look at each of these sufferers in turn, starting with Jemima. Just before I began my review I was approached by Mavis Clenton whose daughter Rebecca had died of *anorexia nervosa* a year previously. Mavis sent me copies of some of Rebecca's poems, one of which, entitled *Dr Sneddon and Me*, read as follows:

I You are getting precisely nowhere, my dear!
   I shrugged and pretended not to hear.
   Come along now, you know what you've got to do
   It's all up to you, dear,
   It's all up to you.

II You'll remember me best by a tombstone engraving:
   'Here lies Rebecca, a girl not worth saving,

Here rot her bones, her intestines, her skin,
Here rots the torment that once writhed within,
Here rots the voice that proclaimed it could win!
Here rots the spineless sick wreck who gave in.'

III I shall gravely reflect by your tombstone, my dear,
You were no good on earth so you're better off here.
As well you know, dear, I did my best
You just didn't try so you're best laid to rest.
Your dull protestations, quite frankly, were boring.
Believe me, they went on so long that ignoring
them all was the only thing that I could do!
Anyway, as I've said, it was all up to you.

IV They're buried forever, those claims that you'd do it,
That you'd alter your life-style for good, and stick to it.
It was plain common sense, dear, if only you'd tried
I can't be contrite, dear, it's your fault you died!
If you'd wanted to do it, my dear girl, you would have.
   For Christ's sake! I shouldn't be here if I could have,
   Here, rotting in my grave,
   Insipid soul that would not save
                      itself.

V Oh dear!
That silly bulimic is dead
Well, it *was* her own fault;
She was quite off her head.

When I read it I realised it could have been written by and
about Jemima Biggs. However, I was hopeful, but by no means
certain, that the fate that had befallen 21-year-old Rebecca,
would be averted by 22-year-old Jemima.

After graduating with first class honours, Jemima decided
she wanted to go for a higher degree. Before she sorted out her
future education she took a job as a live-in au pair with a
sympathetic family in London. Although she was far from
completely overcoming her problems I felt her attitude had

changed enough to ensure immediate survival, and gradual improvement in the long term. There were several reasons for my limited optimism. One was her acknowledgment that life could have highs instead of the perpetual grey lows to which she previously thought she was committed. Thus, when she was down, and she still had periods when she felt very depressed, she knew that she was capable of experiencing joy. And this in turn gave her a glimmer of hope.

Jemima had also discovered that there was a family history of depression (as there had also been, as it happens, with Rebecca). This relieved the guilt she felt over the sadness she knew she imposed upon her family. Her depression had not originated with her. It had been handed down to her in her genetic make-up, for which she was not responsible. Also she had expanded to beyond her immediate family the range of people with whom she had more than superficial relationships. Another noteworthy change was her awareness that she was not alone in harbouring morbid thoughts and finding her physical shape so revoltingly large that she felt compelled to reduce it by starving herself. Finally she was aware that she really was killing herself.

It was Jon Levy who commented that of the three patients we filmed in Ireland it was Neal Jackson, the paranoiac, in whom the difference before and after his encounter with the dolphin was most pronounced. When he returned home from his first visit to Ireland he threw his bag ahead of him as he entered the house and declared, 'Mum, I can do anything now.'

Such unrestrained self-confidence did not remain a permanent feature of his personality. As the weeks passed the pessimism, which earlier had exacerbated his depression, crept back. It was a negative force that worked against him whenever he set a new objective. However, after several setbacks he gained a place in a college and was studying photography full time. He was hopeful that when he had completed the course he would be able to get a job involving photography. He still had his girlfriend Sarah and spent most of his spare time with her. The change in his response to the dolphin from sheer terror to supreme confidence proved that he could overcome a challenge. Nobody, least of all Neal, would deny that this played a significant role in helping him rebuild his confidence when he felt low.

If the concept behind Operation Sunflower was eventually proved to be totally erroneous, would it have been worthwhile? Yes. If only for the happiness it brought into the lives of Bill Bowell and his family. Bill was a changed man and after his first meeting with a dolphin he had no hesitation in saying so himself. He attributed his recovery to the dolphin.

When my daughter Melanie, who had produced the two most beautiful grand-daughters in the world for my delight, heard this she felt she could express her scepticism with her normal candour.

'Dad, you are a famous charismatic person. What you have done for Bill is like Chris Bonington taking me to the top of Everest. If I felt depressed before I went I certainly wouldn't when I got back. Don't you think it's *you* who has changed Bill, not the dolphin?'

I said that in Bill's case I thought it was a combination of both the dolphin and myself. I also told her, that had I been on holiday with Bill and taken him out in an inflatable to see a seal, say, then I felt with considerable certainty that the immense improvement he had made since his first meeting with Simo would not have happened.

I suggested to my daughter that an essential element in what had happened was opening Bill's mind to the possibility that meeting a dolphin could help him. In that respect I admitted that my contribution was highly significant, as indeed it had been with all three patients. As a result of my review there was absolutely no doubt in my mind that Tricia, Jemima, Neal and Bill had all been changed as a direct result of their respective encounters with dolphins. I felt that any sensitive investigator could get a good idea of the extent of these changes by interviewing them and listening to their own accounts of their lives, experiences and feelings. In the end, I reckoned roughly the same stories would emerge regardless of who asked the questions because the facts were available for those who chose to ferret them out.

I also came to the conclusion that none of them, not even Bill, had been cured. I made this point as strongly as I could at the meeting in London. However, when Bill and Jemima stood up and expressed their own views on Operation Sunflower, none of the audience, myself included, could deny that as a result of their dolphin therapy they were better able to handle and respond to the problems their depression brought upon them.

Exchanging Brain Waves
with Dolphins

Analysing *what* happened to the four main human characters in this book is relatively straightforward: trying to determine *how* the changes in them took place, is altogether more difficult, for it takes us away from facts and into the realms of speculation.

After I had given my playshop at the College of Psychic Studies suggestions on how dolphins raised human spirits arrived on my desk from a wide variety of sources. Among them was a letter I received from Jill Miller, a natural health therapist which drew my attention to a recent study in which light was found to be beneficial for the relief of depression. Knowing of the influence sunshine had on the moods of some members of my own family, I could well understand and appreciate the cutting from *Here's Health* magazine (February 1988) which was enclosed with her letter. It dealt with what were described as the 'winter blues' and quoted the case of Jennifer Eastwood, a manic depressive, whose depressions came on only in the dark winter months between October and March. Her problems were relieved when she used a full spectrum light box in her office. One explanation offered in the article involved the pineal gland, sometimes known as the third eye, which produces the mood changing hormone melatonin. Jill noted that when I described Bill's meeting with the dolphin I touched my forehead indicating what I described as an invisible bridge forming between them. She wondered if there were a connection between the benefit of light therapy beamed into the pineal area and what the dolphin appeared to be attempting to do. Several people had suggested that when Bill and the dolphin were suspended, face to face, Dorad was actually directing a beam of inaudible ultrasonic pulses into the human's head, thereby giving him a natural radiation treatment of the dolphin kind – with no harmful side-effects.

Before my visit to Australia I might have dismissed this theory as too fanciful to be worthy of serious consideration. Afterwards I tried to imagine how Charles Darwin felt when he returned to England from his epic scientific odyssey aboard HMS *Beagle*. He could not reconcile his observations on the diversity of plants and animals, especially the closely related finches on the Galapagos Islands, with the accepted explanation of the day for their presence on earth. So he published his observations and thoughts knowing full well that they would be highly controversial, and would alienate him from those who believed implicitly in divine creation. By blazing the trail Darwin made it easier for me to open my mind to the possibility that much of what had been instilled in me as incontrovertible during my formative years was open to question.

I realised that most of my thinking was mechanical and had come about because I lived in a world dominated and regulated largely by machines. In Australia, however, my mind was opened to other aspects of our existence that were not quantifiable. I was encouraged in this direction by Lyall Watson, with whom I shared a pleasant day at his home in Ireland, and by the work of Laurence and Lorne Blair who spent ten years exploring the Indonesian Archipelago. At Long Horuk, the Blairs made contact with a semi-nomadic community of mystics and dream wanderers and met Nanyet, the philosopher and shaman of the community, who possessed the healing touch. He told them about Aping, a global tribal consciousness, that binds all tribes and creatures together as one. Nanyet attempted to link the two British explorers with the Aping through tongue chanting in unison with the fifty men, women and children who crouched with them on the floor of a longhouse in the glimmer of a single oil-lamp.

The Blairs' book, *Ring of Fire*, tells how Nanyet placed the palm of his hand on Laurence's scalp and induced a warm current to trickle through his head and his spine. The book concludes with an account of 'Dynamo Jack', a healer and manipulator of unseen energies, who could send a powerful electrical pulse through a man's arm, could push a chopstick through a plank of wood and set fire to a piece of newspaper without a match, using energy he gathered from the earth and the sky.

I wish I could have enjoyed reading about such things without asking 'Why?' or 'How?', but I couldn't. It was the same when it came to witnessing and hearing about the mystical effect dolphins had on so many people – I had to attempt to find an explanation.

I could see that other factors came into play besides just contact with a dolphin. There was always a combination of circumstances. For instance, the encounters all took place in water, sea water. Our blood is saline, and it has been suggested that its osmotic pressure is the same as that of the sea water from which we evolved millions of years ago. Immersion in sea water can be likened to making a link with our ancestral past. Besides, water is a much better conductor of sounds and vibrations than air, and so it puts us in more intimate contact, so to speak, with the dolphin. And before we are born we live and grow in a safe aqueous environment, called amniotic fluid, inside our mothers. Immersing oneself in the sea is a stress relieving process which has been likened to a return to the womb. Indeed this concept, identified in the 1950s by Dr John Lilly, has advanced steadily to a stage where special tanks, or chambers, are commercially available and in them a 'floater' lies on his or her back in salt water heated to just below body temperature. Isolated in semi-darkness, floaters drift into a state of pleasurable relaxation which may be enhanced by music from underwater speakers. The benefits are both physical and mental – muscle tension being relieved and the sense of blurred boundaries calming the mind.

Floatation has now become a way of life for many people, particularly artists, who find it increases their creativity.

According to American scientists, this comes about because the freedom from gravity and external stimuli activates the right side of the brain, which is associated with intuition and imagination. Dr Thomas Budzynski claims that once the right side is activated, the brain can absorb information more freely. Support for this theory comes from tests on language students who were better able to learn new words while floating. Yet being in the sea with a dolphin is seldom a wholly relaxing experience; moments of peacefully floating are usually swiftly followed by bouts of vigorous activity.

Hydrotherapy is now a well established practice for helping the repair of physical disabilities. When coupled with suitable counselling and aquatic game play, it can also relieve anxiety-related problems. Having seen Cookie Harkin running her pre- and post-natal aquatic programmes in Melbourne, I have no doubt that her techniques would go a long way to preventing and relieving the depression that many mothers experience after giving birth.

In 1988, after seventeen years spent carefully developing her Babyswim programmes, Cookie Harkin set up a dolphin project to extend the already excellent relationship her babies have with water to the open sea and dolphins. Cookie has a hunch that the brain impulses of babies before and after birth are on the same wavelength as those of dolphins and whales, thereby giving rise to telepathic exchanges.

Alpha, and perhaps more importantly theta brain waves, which are associated with vivid imagery and creative thoughts, have been shown to be produced by monks in deep meditative states, and by floatation. Furthermore, they may continue to be produced for weeks after the initial generation process is terminated. So, in theory at least, babies producing and exchanging brain waves with dolphins could grow into children with exceptional talents, though I strongly suspect that it will not be possible to separate and measure the 'dolphin factor' in the development of the lucky children involved in Cookie's project. But does that matter if their lives are spiritually more fulfilled?

In May 1989, at the Dolphin Research Center in Florida, I was able to watch a unique experiment being conducted by an American psychotherapist, Dr David Nathanson, who was working with devoted parents whose children faced uncertain futures due to various mental disorders or brain damage. He was using dolphins in elective capacity to encourage children with learning difficulties, by giving brief lessons in the presence of dolphins. When the child successfully mastered a problem, he or she was rewarded by swimming with the dolphins. So encouraging were the results of early experiments that Dr Nathanson proposed to expand them into a full scientific study in which he would also conduct lessons in the presence of other responsive animals. He hopes to provide proof that would satisfy those who demanded scientific evidence to support the theory that dolphins can help children and adults suffering from brain damage.

For the dolphins these experiments are part of a great game; indeed for them life seems to be a game most of the time. Will Dr Nathanson be able to separate out the benefits his subjects will receive as the result of the play element imparted by the dolphins into the learning programme? One American scientist who would consider this an important consideration is Dr Fred Donaldson, who believes that 'play short circuits the human thinking process, going directly to the heart'. As a result of his own extensive studies, Dr Donaldson is careful to distinguish play from sport and competitions in which playing to win becomes the objective. Winning and losing he sees as extinguishing the very essence of play, which is to bring the participants into joyful harmony with one another, not to separate them into winners and losers.

In Florida I also met Carolyn Brooks-Kidd, a counsellor who incorporated dolphin swims to help people overcome emotional problems when she conducted BRETH workshops. I was already familiar with the acronym which stands for Breath Releasing Energy for Transformation and Healing, because it was one of the spiritual healing techniques involving conscious breathing and meditation used by Kamala Hope-Campbell who had organised the Whale and Dolphin conference in Australia. At that gathering it was suggested that there was a net of dolphin force around the earth. Furthermore, some people claim they can tune into it, even if they have never seen a dolphin.

One person to maintain she could do this was Gwenda Stephens, who had a grown-up daughter and lived in Warwickshire. She nursed emotionally disturbed children and would listen to tapes of New Age music to help her relax after work. It all began, she says, after she started to collect crystals.

I was given a lovely ceramic dolphin, and loved to hold it, finding it very calming. Then one day as I lay meditating, I just seemed to slip out of my body and swam into a dry ocean of space. There I was joined by a beautiful dolphin. He was very close, yet did not touch. We swam as one, we were one, yet in body worlds apart. We moved as in a ballet, spiralled, dived, soared, turned, rolled. I was totally safe and secure, the ocean seemed as endless as the universe. Eventually, the dolphin swam away, returned, and swam away again, showing me it was time to part. Very reluctantly I re-entered my body − left that other world without gravity, a world full of unconditional love.

To begin with, I kept to the same routine of tape and meditation, but as time went on, I could become aware of dolphins (sometimes two or more) just by thinking about them. They would appear (sensed) and swim round, curious, as if they wondered why I had called them.

I believe that so called spirit dolphins are not ghost dolphins. I believe they appear through telepathic pathways, in the same way as they 'speak' to each other over long distances.

I believe, too, there may be a connection between dolphins and crystals − the latter are known to be able to receive and store signals. Legend has it dolphins once walked on the land when crystals were used extensively for communication. Now they are back, as a time release capsule. But have we gone so far down the path of aggression and greed that we stop listening – when the very planet screams for us to do so? We readily listen to signals from satellites out in space through our TV sets. Yet we say 'madness' when the dolphin pleads with us to listen – not for his sake, for ours.

In the autumn of 1987, before Gwenda made these extraordinary connections with dolphins, she was given a piece of rock quartz. Here is how she describes the effect it had on her.

I felt so drawn to it, I have made pieces part of my family ever since. Their beauty, shape and colour are a joy to see, but they also emit a vibration that I can 'feel'. It can alter if the crystal is approached by a 'negative' person.

When Gwenda asked me to run my hands over her collection of crystals, she said I should feel their warmth. I certainly admired their jewel-like brilliance, colour and beauty, but I had to admit to her, in all honesty, that I was unable to feel anything. Perhaps I was too insensitive. This does not make the experience any less real for Gwenda. Maybe, at some later date, I will shed whatever it is that is blocking the path. I am all too aware that every cubic centimetre of space in every room, in every house, in every town, in every city, in every country, in every rainforest, over every desert and under every ocean in the world is teeming with waves of energy carrying information and messages. To speak of nothing else, there are hundreds of television and radio channels that we can tune into anywhere on our planet. It is almost impossible to imagine how much information is all around us and passing through us, every moment of our lives. All we need is an aerial and a couple of micro chips to tap into it.

Consider another situation. Our bodies are full of electrical currents. We do not need to implant detectors in our hearts to measure their electrical activity. To produce electrocardiograms (ECGs) we simply have to attach electrodes to our chests.

Perhaps even more remarkable is our ability to detect electrical activity in that immensely complex organ inside our heads, the brain, by simply sticking electrodes on the outside of the strong box with which it is protected, the skull. Now we take ECGs and EEGs for granted, but how could we have started to comprehend them before Faraday first demonstrated electricity to the Royal Society? All this electrical activity has been going on inside our mammalian bodies for millions of years, yet it is only in the last century that we have come to understand it. We have not invented electricity; we have simply discovered how to generate, manipulate, identify and measure it.

No scientist can say for sure that global dolphin consciousness does or does not exist, or how long it will be before we can identify and measure it. So what should we do in the mean time?

I think we should at least be open to the suggestion that it is there. For if we do not we might well find ourselves in a similar position to those who swore the earth was flat, as it appeared to those who could see only as far as the nearest horizon.

You might well ask where all this speculation is taking us. I will tell you. It leads me to propose that as the result of the explosion of technology we humans now find ourselves as the single most powerful influence on the planet earth. Furthermore, we have reached a crossroads and the dolphins are signalling the way to go.

I know that sounds even more far fetched than many of the other ideas we have considered in this chapter. But let me tell you one final story that is improbable − but true.

· 23 ·

The Wall Crumbles

It is October 1988, and I am sitting in my study. The phone rings.

'My name is Anna Studholme,' says a friendly, cultured, female voice. 'I am looking for someone to write a booklet on the nature of dolphins, and all the paths I have tried have led to you.'

I explain that at this very moment I happen to have a pen in my hand and am writing a book – this book – about the influence of dolphins on people suffering from depression. Once I get going it's hard to stop. So I tell her a little of Bill's remarkable story.

'It sounds as if you are just the person I need!'

Anna then explains that she is employed by GCI Sterling, a large public relations company, and is working on a highly confidential project for one of their clients, a multinational company seeking a new management policy. The company is considerate to its employees and conscious of its social, economic and environmental responsibilities in the many countries where it manufactures and sells its products. The top echelons of the company are unhappy, however, about the 'shark and carp' mentality which prevails in big business, extending to life in general. It is an approach that is all too familiar to me, namely, that if you don't aggressively attack and overwhelm the competition, then you yourself are gobbled up. What the company wants is to develop a new strategy, based upon a dolphin-like philosophy, which they will not only apply to their business ventures, but will also introduce into the day-to-day running of their affairs.

I cannot believe what I am hearing. Is this some kind of hoax? I ask myself. When she mentions the company's name I am even more astounded. I have several of their electrical appliances in the house.

'Let me get this straight,' I say to Anna, trying to suppress my incredulity. 'You want a dolphin attitude to permeate through the whole of the business – from top management down to the most junior employee? You're not really serious, are you?'

'Oh yes I am,' Anna replies. 'The idea has already been approved by the company directors.'

I find the notion of a board of directors responsible for handling millions of dollars, sitting round a table and talking about adopting a dolphin-like attitude to business, just too improbable to contemplate, and I tell her so. But, she assures me, that is exactly what has happened. It is a radical change, and to help their staff identify, understand and promote this new direction in company policy, they need a booklet on the lifestyle of dolphins. So again I am asked if I will help.

I have seen and studied at very close quarters the way in which dolphins could change, indeed *had* changed individual people. But the idea that they could directly influence the manner in which a multinational company conducts its affairs in a thriving competitive society is beyond anything I could ever have dreamt.

As I set down my thoughts on the subject my hope was that the dolphin ethos I was attempting to capture in words would gradually permeate to other sections of society. Publication of the booklet late in 1989 coincided with the political upheaval in Eastern Europe where social change was taking place that would have been unthinkable a few months earlier. The Berlin Wall was torn down when the reason for its existence suddenly vaporised. Arms were reduced. As the last decade of the millennium dawned unimaginable changes also came to the Soviet Union, South Africa and Central America. Everywhere the dolphin values I had identified – such as living harmoniously in caring communities – looked as though they were being adopted as key political objectives. Yet these waves of glasnost sentiment were secondary to the all-pervasive desire among people for greater freedom, which to me was the very essence of the dolphin spirit.

While world leaders struggled to control the watershed of political reform in which they were engulfed, I made a flying visit to the West Indies to see a friendly dolphin I had heard about. There I discovered that an opportunity existed which might enable us to take a quantum leap forward in our understanding of the human/dolphin relationship. The situation was not without parallel in the world arena where politicians were attempting to decide their respective goals and knew that reaching them would entail resolving a host of different attitudes and interests. I found myself stepping into an arena in which two intelligent species, with even greater differences than those of the cultures of east and west Europe, were spontaneously coming together closer than ever before. By so doing they pressed forward for resolution an understanding of their respective needs, and in the case of humans, their aspirations also. It was a new challenge and I looked in two directions for inspiration.

Firstly, there were the dolphins themselves who, by means which I still could not identify precisely, seemed to be directing my life. Secondly, there was a rapidly expanding circle of humans, from greatly different backgrounds to my own, who had been imbued with the dolphin spirit and were blazing their own dolphin trails.

My enthusiasm to continue probing the secrets of the dolphin's mind was fuelled by the first results of Operation Sunflower. A psychotherapist at Oxford University was so impressed with the changes he saw in Bill Bowell that he visited Ireland himself in the company of a fellow doctor, who was more than sceptical, a senior clinical research nurse and a zoology student. After three idyllic days, in which they all got into the sea with the dolphin, every member of the group was affected in his or her own way by the experience. Seeing Bill's beaming face when they returned to Oxford served only to confirm their new-found conviction that something very special was going on in Ireland.

The way was now open to carry forward my investigations with the remarkable dolphin I had encountered in the warm waters of the Caribbean.

Postscript

When I first conceived the idea of an 'audio pill' to capture the mood changing essence of dolphins my intention was to see if it would help people suffering from depression. To find out how successful, or otherwise, this idea was, each *Dolphin Dreamtime* tape was accompanied by an assessment form on which recipients were asked to record their experiences.

After more than one thousand tapes had been distributed it was clear that most patients benefited. Many people not suffering from mental illness also sent in reports of their reactions on being taken, in their minds via the tape, into the dolphin's world. Their completed forms indicated that they were affected in a wide variety of ways. A high proportion simply went to sleep. Among those was a general practitioner who suffered from insomnia, especially when she was on call. After listening to the tape she had her best night's sleep in years. A midwife who had volunteered to investigate the effects of the tape on mothers suffering post-natal depression discovered that it was beneficial during delivery, helping with relaxation between contractions. Many students reported that listening to the tape helped to dispel pre-examination nerves.

The study continues. If you would like to participate please write to: International Dolphin Watch, North Ferriby, Humberside HU14 3ET.

Should you decide to join the IDW Supporters Club, which has a world-wide membership, you will receive reports on Operation Sunflower as well as being kept informed on many other dolphin-related topics.

Bibliography

Anthony Alpers, *Dolphins*, London: John Murray, 1960.

Bruce Bernard, *Vincent by himself*, London: Orbis Publishing, 1985.

Laurence Blair, *Ring of Fire*, London: Bantam Press, 1988.

Robin Brown, *The Lure of the Dolphin*, New York: Avon Books, 1979.

Bruce Chatwin, *The Songlines*, London: Jonathan Cape, 1988.

Jacques-Yves Cousteau, *Dolphins*, London: Cassell, 1974.

Wade Doak, *Dolphin Dolphin*, Auckland: Hodder and Stoughton, 1981.

Wade Doak, *Ocean Planet*, Auckland: Hodder and Stoughton, 1984.

Wade Doak, *Encounters with Whales and Dolphins*, Auckland: Hodder and Stoughton, 1988.

Horace Dobbs, *Camera Underwater*, London: Focal Press, 1963.

Horace Dobbs, *Follow a Wild Dolphin*, London: Souvenir Press, 1977.

Horace Dobbs, *Save the Dolphins*, London: Souvenir Press, 1981.

Horace Dobbs, *The Magic of Dolphins*, Guildford: Lutterworth Press, 1984.

Horace Dobbs, *Tale of Two Dolphins*, London: Jonathan Cape, 1987.

Peter Evans, *The Natural History of Whales and Dolphins*, London: Christopher Helm, 1987.

Karl-Eric Fichtelius and Sverre Sjölander, *Man's Place: Intelligence in Whales, Dolphins, and Humans*, London: Gollancz, 1973.

Ronnie Fitzgibbon, *The Dingle Dolphin*, Athlone: Temple Printing, 1988.

Elizabeth Gawain, *The Dolphin's Gift*, Mill Valley: Whatever Publishing, 1981.

Richard Harrison, *Whales, Dolphins and Porpoises*, London: Merehurst Press, 1988.

John Lilly, *Man and Dolphin*, New York: Doubleday, 1961.

John Lilly, *The Mind of the Dolphin*, New York: Doubleday, 1967.

Ronald Lockley, *Whales, Dolphins and Porpoises*, Newton Abbot: David and Charles, 1979.

Joan McIntyre, *Mind in the Waters*, New York: Scribner, 1974.

Lana Miller, *Call of the Dolphins*, Portland: Rainbow Bridge Publishing, 1989.

Jim Nollman, *Dolphin Dreamtime — Talking to the Animals*, London: Anthony Blond, 1985.

Richard O'Barry, *Behind the Dolphin Smile*, Chapel Hill: Algonquin Books, 1988.

Bibliography

Maurice O'Sullivan: *Twenty Years A-Growing*, Oxford: Oxford University Press, 1953.

Giorgio Pilleri, *The Secrets of the Blind Dolphins*, Karachi: Sind Wildlife Management Board, 1980.

Frank Robson, *Thinking Dolphins, Talking Whales*, Wellington: A. H. and A. W. Reed, 1976.

Frank Robson, *Pictures in the Dolphin Mind*, Dobbs Ferry: Sheridan House, 1988.

Rosamund Rowe, *Feet Upon a Rock*, Dunedin: Caveman Press, 1981.

Tim Severin, *The Brendan Voyage*, London: Hutchinson, 1978.

Erik Sidenbladh, *Water Babies*, London: Adam and Charles Black, 1983.

Robert Stenuit, *The Dolphin: Cousin to Man*, London: J. M. Dent, 1969.

Leo Szilard, *The Voice of the Dolphins*, London: Victor Gollancz, 1961.

Lyall Watson, *Whales of the World*, London: Hutchinson, 1981.

Heathcote Williams, *Whale Nation*, London: Jonathan Cape, 1988.

Heathcote Williams, *Falling for a Dolphin*, London: Jonathan Cape, 1988.

Heathcote Williams, *Sacred Elephant*, London: Jonathan Cape, 1989.

Timothy Wyllie, *The Deta Factor: Dolphins, Extra-terrestrials, and Angels*, Farmingdale: Coleman Publishing, 1984.